LITERATURE

WORKS

A Collection of Readings

COLLECTION 3/2

Silver Burdett Ginn
A Division of Simon & Schuster
160 Gould Street
Needham Heights, MA 02194

Developed and produced in association with Ligature

ISBN: 0-663-59038-8   1 2 3 4 5 6 7 8 9 10 VHP 01 00 99 98 97 96 95

*L*ITERATURE WORKS

A Collection of Readings

COLLECTION 3 / 2

THEMES

Tales from Around the World

Taking Care of the Earth

Meeting Challenges

SILVER BURDETT GINN

Needham, MA   Parsippany, NJ

Atlanta, GA   Deerfield, IL   Irving, TX   Santa Clara, CA

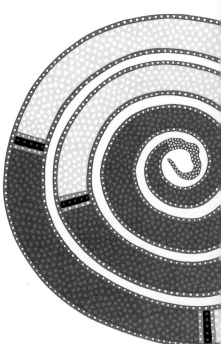

Tales from Around the World

There's so much that we share, and it's time we're aware, it's a small world after all.

"It's a Small World"
by Richard M. Sherman
and Robert B. Sherman

Australia

Asia

Contents

Books from Your Classroom Library

The Tale of Rabbit and Coyote by Tony Johnston tells how Rabbit tricks Coyote and escapes the cookpot.

The Cricket Warrior by Margaret and Raymond Chang tells the story of Wei nian, who loses the fighting cricket that is his family's key to survival. But with the help of a mysterious old man, Wei nian is able to save the family's farm.

Story Zone

Do you want to be a storyteller? Or a story keeper? Stories are hidden everywhere, and you can find out where in the *Theme Magazine Story Zone.*

THE TALE OF RABBIT AND COYOTE

Tony Johnston • Tomie dePaola

THE CRICKET WARRIOR
A Chinese Tale

Retold by Margaret and Raymond Chang
Illustrated by Warwick Hutton

Need to cook up a story? We've got a recipe! Plus: Hoop Scoop

story
Zone

inside
If Things
Could Talk...
Urban Myths
Here Comes
Trickster!

tales from
around
the world

Author and Illustrator at Work

 Stefan Czernecki was born in Germany. His family moved first to Brazil and then settled in Canada. Czernecki did not speak English when he first moved to Canada and school was very difficult for him. Now he volunteers to help other Canadian immigrants get used to life in their new country. His home in Calgary is filled with his collection of folk art. Czernecki and Timothy Rhodes wrote the story for "The Singing Snake" together. Czernecki did the illustrations.

 Timothy Rhodes enjoyed writing and publishing his own picture books when he was a child. He remembers that one of his books was about a flea who lived on a dog and collected the dog's hair. Some of Rhodes' favorite things to read when he was a child were fairy tales by the brothers Grimm and Hans Christian Andersen. Rhodes went to elementary school in a one-room schoolhouse, the same one his father and grandfather had attended.

Long ago, on a great island in the middle of the ocean, there lived a collection of creatures found nowhere else in the world. They all chattered at once, and their voices were harsh and loud. The island was the noisiest place you could imagine.

Tired of the raucous sounds, Old Man said he would make a musical instrument in honor of the creature who developed the most beautiful singing voice. All day and all night the animals and birds sang and sang, each trying to sing louder than the others in order to be noticed by Old Man. The voices were more musical, but the sound of so many different animals singing at the same time made such a din that no one could sleep.

"Enough," said Old Man one day. "We will all gather together, have a proper contest, and settle this once and for all. I need some sleep."

A large, colorful snake listened to Old Man and thought about his chances. He wanted to win the contest, but he knew that he had only an average singing voice. It would never be judged the best. He listened carefully to the other contestants.

"Lark has the most beautiful voice," Snake finally decided.

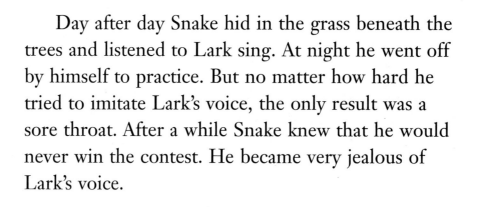

Day after day Snake hid in the grass beneath the trees and listened to Lark sing. At night he went off by himself to practice. But no matter how hard he tried to imitate Lark's voice, the only result was a sore throat. After a while Snake knew that he would never win the contest. He became very jealous of Lark's voice.

One day Lark flew down from a tree near Snake and began to hop about on the ground, pecking at insects. Snake noticed how very small Lark was.

"Hmmm." He was getting an idea.

"If I swallowed Lark whole and was careful not to harm her, and held her just at the back of my throat, then I'm sure I could *borrow* her voice for the song festival."

Once Snake had made up his mind, he quickly swallowed Lark. She began to sing in protest, but her song appeared to be coming from Snake.

This will work perfectly, thought Snake. He hastened off to the festival.

Whenever he encountered another animal along the way, Snake would smile, taking care that his teeth blocked Lark's escape.

When Snake smiled, the light shone through his teeth, and Lark began to sing.

Everyone thought that Snake was singing, and they marveled at his magnificent voice.

"Your voice is certainly much improved from last year," said Platypus.

"Snake has obviously been taking singing lessons," remarked Lyrebird, somewhat peevishly.

"I wish I had a voice as enchanting as Snake's," whined Dingo.

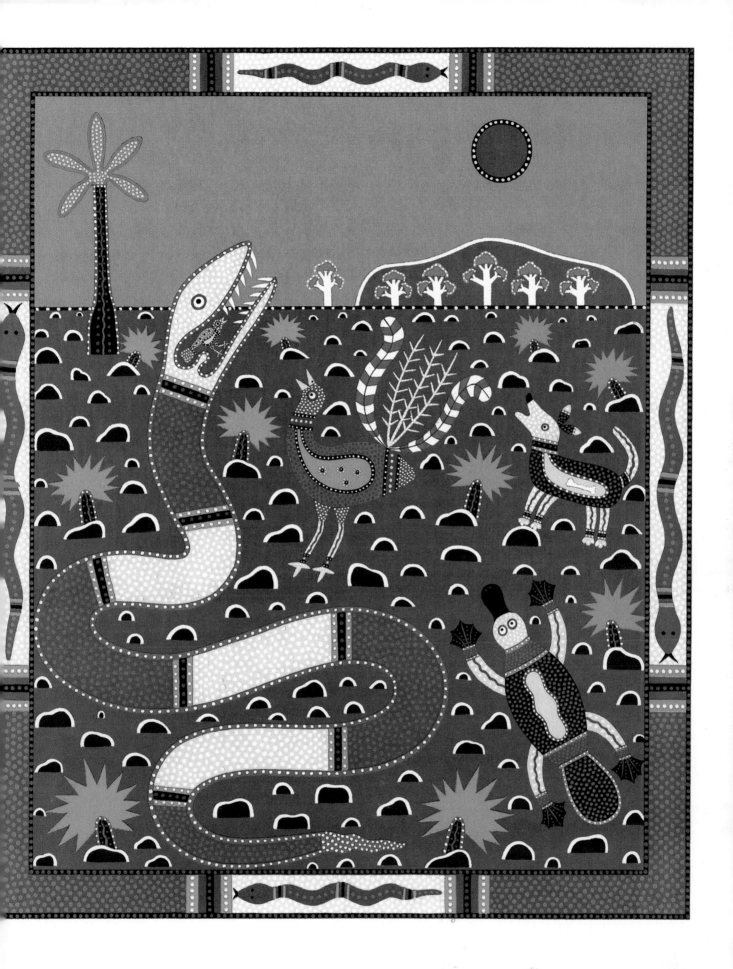

Snake smiled serenely and continued on his way. As he approached the festival, he met more and more creatures. They all expressed amazement at his brilliant voice. Even the other birds were filled with wonder when Snake sang.

"It's almost as if Snake were a bird," said Emu admiringly.

"Such a sorrowful and anguished song," added Cockatoo. "It makes me want to cry."

The song festival was ready to begin. When all the participants were assigned places on the program for the contest, Snake didn't wait his turn. He squeezed his way between Blue-tongued Lizard and Long-necked Tortoise to the front of the line. Then he reared himself up, held his head in the air, and smiled. The sunlight struck Lark, and she began to sing.

Her song was so sad and so beautiful that every animal was soon in tears. Even Crocodile's tears were real.

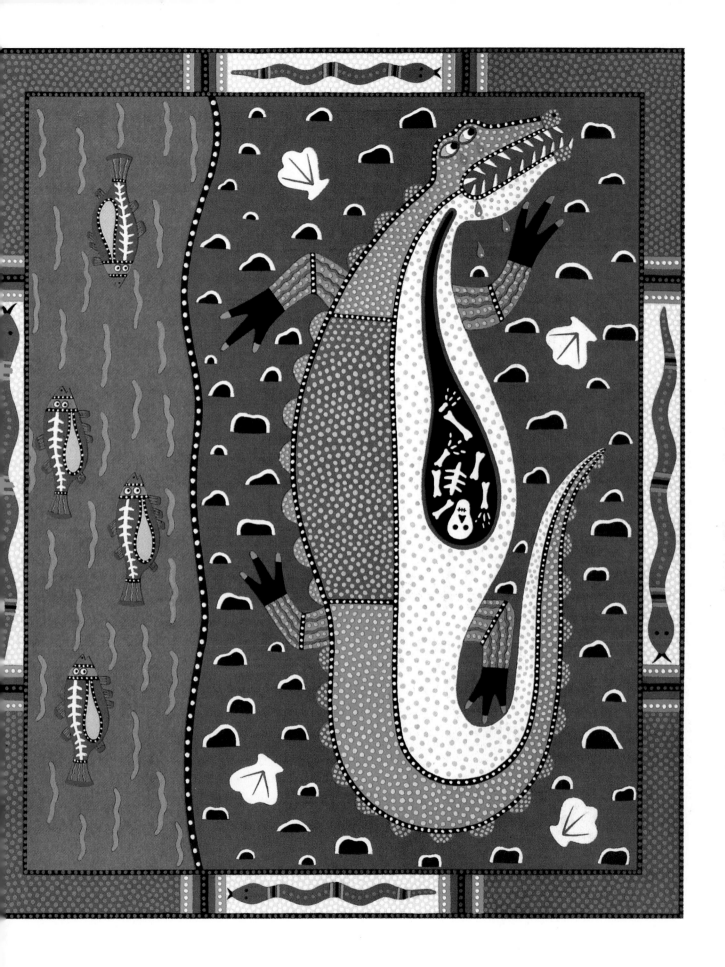

The other contestants agreed that Snake's song was so fine and his voice so perfect that he should win the contest. Red Spiny Lizard, Echidna, Honey Ant, Frilled Lizard, Kookaburra, Pelican, Frog, Wallaby, Lorikeet, Kangaroo, and the others did not even bother to compete.

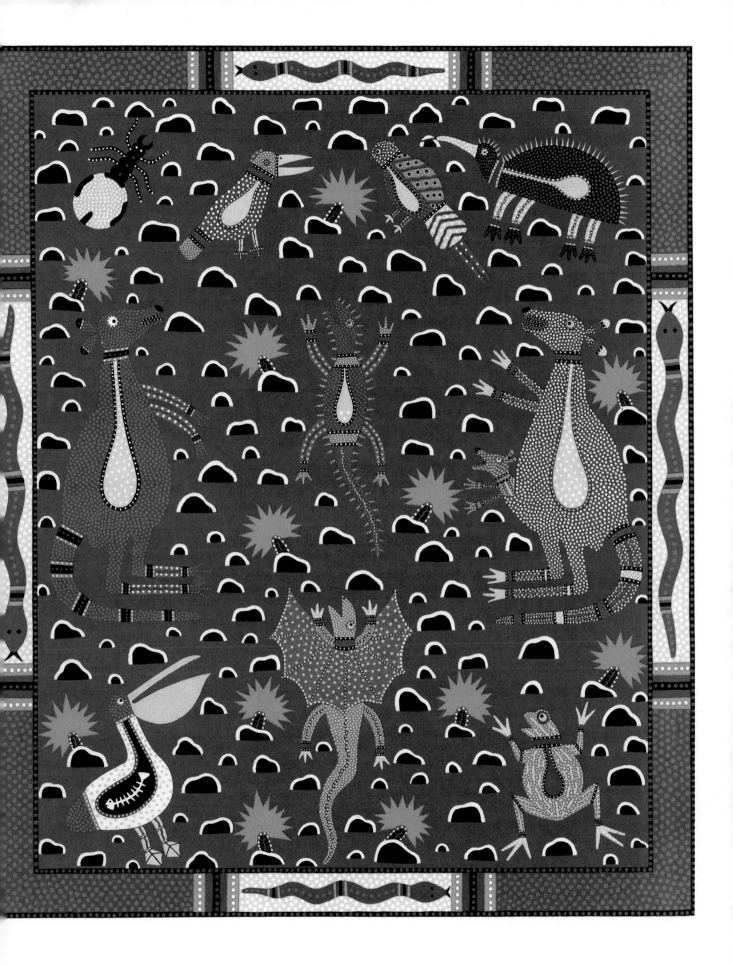

Old Man agreed and named Snake the winner of the contest. "I will go now," he said, " and make my musical instrument in Snake's shape."

After Old Man had gone, the animals gathered around Snake. "Please, Snake, sing us an encore," they begged.

Snake smiled again. But this time, instead of singing, Lark began to scratch at Snake's throat with her little feet. Scratch, scratch. Scratch, scratch. Scratch, scratch.

Snake's cheeks bulged out as he tried not to cough. His eyes bulged, too. A faint sound like a hiss came from his mouth.

Lark continued to scratch with her little feet. Scratch, scratch. Scratch, scratch. Scratch, scratch.

Finally Snake could stand it no longer. With a loud hack, he coughed, and his mouth opened wide. Lark quickly flew to the safety of a tree branch and began to sing a glorious song of freedom.

All the creatures were so delighted with Lark's song that they were distracted for a moment. Snake quickly hid in another tree, pretending he was a branch.

When Lark's song was finished, the creatures noticed that Snake had disappeared. They were very angry. "He cheated us," they said. "He was horrible to Lark."

We should never speak to him again," said Koala.

"Nor trust him," added Flying Squirrel.

When all the animals had gone, Snake came down from the tree. Just as he had reached the ground, Old Man returned with his instrument.

"It looks like you, Snake," Old Man said, showing Snake the great horn that he had made. "The sound isn't as sweet as your singing, but I like it, and it will go well with your voice." Old Man blew into the strange instrument. A low, rich humming filled the air.

Snake said nothing and slithered off into the tall grass in shame.

No one ever did speak to Snake again. After a while he forgot how to speak himself. All he could make was a hissing sound, as if something were going "scratch, scratch—scratch, scratch" in his throat.

Today people call the island where these creatures lived Australia. They call the instrument the Old Man made a didgeridoo, and they refer to someone who cannot be trusted as a snake in the grass.

In Response

A Snake in the Grass People say a sneaky, mean person is "a snake in the grass." Plan and write your own story that tells how this saying came to be.

Create a Musical Instrument What animal, real or imaginary, do you think would have the most beautiful singing voice? Invent a musical instrument shaped like the animal, and draw a picture of it. Tell how to play the instrument and what it will sound like.

Be a Reporter Pretend you are a newspaper reporter. Interview the animals in Old Man's singing contest. Ask them how they felt when they found out that snake cheated.

The Crocodile

If you should meet a crocodile,
Don't take a stick and poke him;
Ignore the welcome
in his smile,
Be careful not to
stroke him.
For as he sleeps
upon the Nile,
He thinner gets
and thinner;
And whene'er
you meet
a crocodile
He's ready
for his
dinner.

Author Unknown

Author and Illustrator at Work

★ Award-winning Author

 Verna Aardema has always been interested in Africa and in story-telling. When she was growing up, she loved telling stories to her friends. Now many of her books are based on folk tales that people in Africa tell aloud. Some of the tales were first heard from African storytellers more than one hundred years ago.

 When **James Grashow** was a child, he never found his birthday presents as much fun to play with as the boxes in which they came. He loved to make things and to draw. In fact, Grashow says art was the only thing he loved to do: "I was never good at math or spelling. I was never a good athlete. But I was good at drawing."

★ Award-winning Book

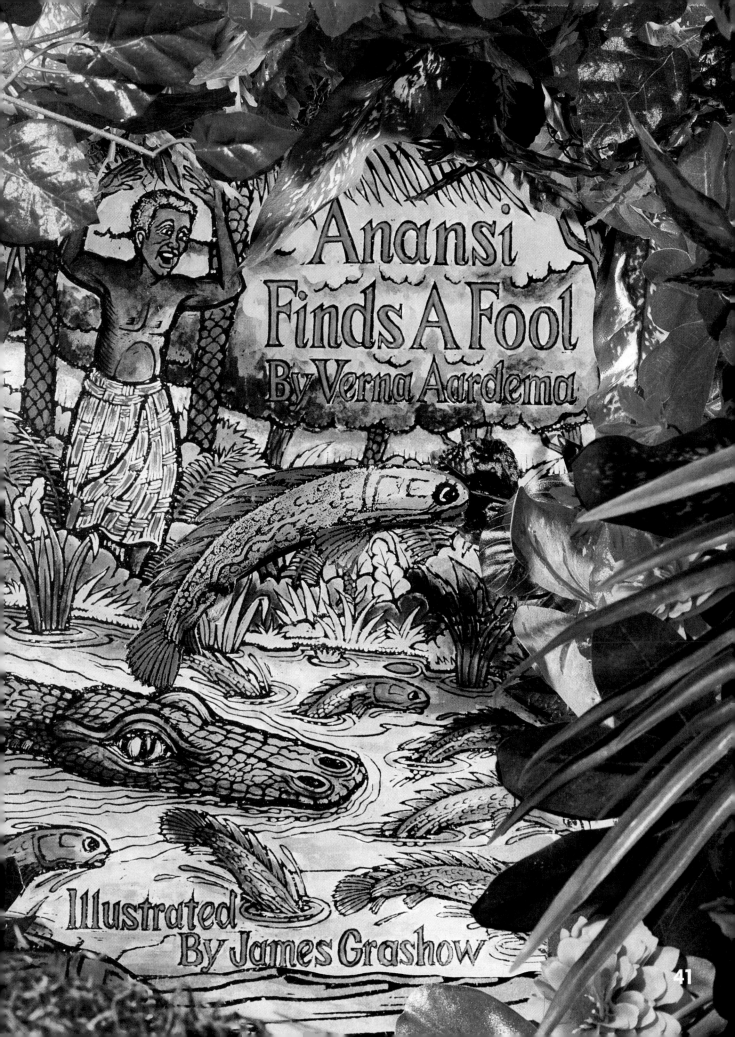

Anansi Finds A Fool
By Verna Aardema

Illustrated By James Grashow

In West Africa there once lived a man named Anansi. He was greedy and lazy and always up to some trick. One morning he announced to Aso, his wife, that he was going into the fishing business.

Aso said, "One of my ears has heard. There remains the other."

Anansi chuckled, *"Huh, Huh, huh."* He said, "I'm going to find a fool for a partner—someone who will do all the work while I get all the fish."

"Ha!" said Aso. "Where will you find such a fool?" She put her water jar on her head and set out for the river.

44

At the riverside Aso met Laluah, the wife of Bonsu. Laluah asked, "Are you well?"

"I am quite well," said Aso. "It's that husband of mine. He said he's going into the fishing business. And he's going to find a fool to help him—someone who will do all the work while he gets all the fish."

Laluah went home and told Bonsu what Aso had said.

Bonsu thought about that for a small time. Then he said, "I'll go fishing with Anansi. I will beat him at his own game!"

Bonsu went to Anansi's house. He said, "Anansi, I'll go fishing with you. Two can catch fish better than one."

Anansi was surprised at Bonsu's offer. And a little uncomfortable too. Bonsu would not be easy to trick. But he said, "All right. First we will have to make a fish trap."

Anansi and Bonsu went looking for material for the trap. They found some raffia palms. And Bonsu said, "Anansi, give me the knife. I'll cut the branches. And your part will be to get tired for me."

"Hold it, man," cried Anansi. "Why should I get tired for you?"

"When work is being done, someone has to get tired," said Bonsu. "If I cut the branches, the least you can do is to take the weariness."

Anansi said, "The tiredness is the worst part! I'll do the cutting myself. And YOU must get tired for ME!"

So Anansi climbed the raffia palm and began slashing off the fronds.

Bonsu sat nearby. And every time Anansi chopped, Bonsu grunted, "Kra . . . UNH, kra . . . UNH, kra . . .UNH!"

Soon there was a great pile of material cut.

Then Bonsu said, "Now you sit down, Anansi. I'll make the trap. Sore fingers and an aching back is what I'll get. But I will do the work, if you will suffer for me."

"Hold it, man" said Anansi. "You are doing fine taking the misery. I'll make the fish trap myself."

While Anansi worked, Bonsu suffered. He wiped his brow, rubbed his back, and moaned, *"Du, du, du."*

Bonsu's fussing was such a diversion that Anansi forgot his own discomfort. By weaving and tying, weaving and tying, he finally finished the trap.

"What a fine fish trap!" exclaimed Bonsu, as he balanced it on his head. "If we meet any people on the way to the river, they will think I made it."

"Wait," cried Anansi. "Why should you get credit for my work?" And he pulled the trap off Bonsu's head and put it on his own.

When the two reached the riverside, Bonsu said, "Anansi, there are crocodiles in the river. Let me set the trap. If I get a leg bitten off, you can die for me."

"Hold it, man," cried Anansi. "Do you take me for a fool? I'll plant the trap myself. If a crocodile gets me, YOU can die for ME!"

Anansi carried the trap into a patch of water reeds near the shore. As he was tying it to a reed stem near the bottom of the river, his groping hand disturbed a crayfish.

Then *kapp!* A huge claw clamped on to his little finger.

"Waaaaaa!" yelled Anansi, as he came splashing out of the water—the crayfish dangling from his hand like a fish at the end of a fish pole.

Bonsu pried the claw off Anansi's finger. Then he said, "This is the biggest crayfish I have ever seen. It will make a fine meal for you and Aso."

"You take it," said Anansi, as he wrapped a leaf around his bleeding finger. "I'll get whatever is in the trap in the morning."

When Laluah saw the fine crayfish that Bonsu had brought, she clapped her hands. And immediately she put the kettle on to boil.

When Anansi arrived home, Aso said, "Well, how did it go?"

"How did what go?" asked Anansi. He was not anxious to tell her anything.

"The fishing business," said Aso.

Anansi said, "The trap is in the water. And whatever is in it in the morning will be all ours.

The next morning, as soon as the darkness was torn aside, Anansi and Bonsu went to look at their fish trap. As they reached the riverside, they saw that the reeds around the trap were agitated.

The two ran *kiliwili* down the bank into the river. They closed the large end of the trap and dragged it out of the water. It was heavy—full of something big and black and coiled! They set it down hastily and backed away.

Then *purup!* The flap on the trap burst open. And out slithered a huge python. Its body was a series of humps and bumps.

"Look!" cried Bonsu. "That snake has swallowed your fish! Count them!"

Anansi counted, "One, two, three, four . . ."

And by that time the python had dragged its loaded body *gu-bu-du* back into the river.

Anansi said, "Bonsu, you can't count that as my turn. I'll have whatever comes into the trap next. And we'll stay right here and watch."

The two men put the trap back into the river.

Time passed, time passed, time passed. At last they heard the *swop* of a fish jumping in the water.

Suddenly *swop . . . swop . . . swop!* The river was full of apopokiki fish leaping in and out of the water—all heading upstream.

Anansi jumped up and began yelling to the fish, "Into the trap! Go into the trap!"

"A crocodile is chasing them!" cried Bonsu.

Then *whoosh!* The fish trap rose up out of the water, spilling fish and revealing the head of a crocodile inside it!

The crocodile thrashed this way and that, trying to shake off the frightening hat. Then it came lumbering up out of the water.

Anansi shinnied up one tree; and Bonsu another. From the trees they watched the crocodile bash their trap against the ground, *BAKATAK! BAKATAK!* Finally it fell away. And the crocodile sashayed back into the water and streaked off after the school of apopokiki.

Anansi and Bonsu climbed down and examined the trap.

Bonsu said, "Sorry, my friend. The trap is finished. But it still does not look too bad. I think I shall take it to the market and sell it."

"Hold it, man," said Anansi. "I didn't get one lone fish from this fishing business—not even a crayfish. And now you want to take the trap away from me! I'll take it and sell it myself."

Anansi took the trap to the market. He sat down beside it and called out, "Fish trap for sale. Fish trap for sale."

People saw that the trap was badly broken. They told the headman of the village.

The headman went to Anansi and said, "Do you think that my people are so ignorant that they will buy a good-for-nothing fish trap? You insult us!"

Then he made Anansi put the trap on his head and walk through the market, crying "No-good fish trap for sale. No-good fish trap for sale."

Anansi's eyes died for shame. The people howled with laughter. And children followed him shouting, *"Nah! Nah! Nah!"*

When it was over, Bonsu came to him and said, "Anansi, you were looking for a fool to go fishing with. You didn't have far to look. You were the fool yourself."

Anansi said, "But, Bonsu, what kind of a partner were you? When all of those people were making fun of me, at least you should have taken the shame!"

61

The next morning Aso and Laluah met again at the river. They saw the flattened water reeds and the trampled shore—the aftermath of their husbands' fishing business.

And when Laluah told Aso how Bonsu had tricked Anansi into doing all the work, Aso laughed so hard, the water jar slipped off her head.

As she caught it, Aso said, "It's a true saying: When you dig a hole for someone else, you will fall into it yourself."

IN RESPONSE

When You Dig a Hole Think of the saying at the end of the story, "When you dig a hole for someone else, you will fall into it yourself." Write a paragraph that tells how the saying was true of Anansi and Bonsu.

Dear Anansi Pretend you are Bonsu, and write a short letter to Anansi. Apologize for tricking Anansi, and tell why you did it.

What's Next? Work with a partner and imagine what will happen the next time Anansi and Bonsu meet. Write what each person will say. Act out the scene for the class.

Story Scene Choose a favorite part of the story and draw a picture of it. You could draw Anansi setting the trap, the crayfish, the crocodile, or any other scene from the story.

The Ant and the Dove

Written by Aesop

A thirsty ant crawled down to the edge of a stream for a drink, but just at that moment the current swelled and the ant was carried away. A dove who was flying by saw the ant, broke off a twig, and threw it into the water. The ant crawled onto the twig and in a moment was washed safely onto dry land.

Later that day a hunter appeared with some sticks smeared with lime and started to set them in position to catch the dove. When the ant saw this, she bit the man sharply on the foot. With a shriek of pain, the hunter dropped the sticks and clutched his foot. The dove, frightened by the noise, flew off.

MORAL
One good turn deserves another.

Author and Illustrator at Work

Shonto Begay is the son of a Navajo medicine man. A medicine man is a Native American who is thought to have the power to cure illness or keep evil away. Begay grew up in Arizona with his fifteen brothers and sisters in a hogan. A hogan is a traditional Navajo house made of earth and wood. Begay's father built the family hogan.

The folk tale you are about to read, "Ma'ii and Cousin Horned Toad," was Begay's favorite story when he was a child.

Ma'ii and Cousin Horned Toad

A TRADITIONAL NAVAJO STORY

SHONTO BEGAY

Up on the mountainside, where the air smells like cedar and pine, Ma'ii paused, and looked back into the sagebrush-covered valley.

He was glad to be away from there. Sagebrush made his nose itch.

He had been trotting along all morning. The sun was now directly over his head. He was hungry. Ma'ii was always hungry.

I think I'll visit my cousin on the other side of the mountain, he thought. *I know he'll feed me good.*

As he ran, his stomach growled. He liked his stomach full, not noisy.

Meanwhile, cousin Horned Toad was out pulling weeds in his cornfield. Wiping sweat off his forehead, he sang while he worked:

"Working every day in my cornfield
Tending it with care
Praying every day in my cornfield
That rain will fill the air
Soon I'll harvest my cornfield
My bounty I'll share
When snow covers my cornfield
Warmth and joy with many fine meals
Friends, neighbors and — "

"Hey, cousin!" Horned Toad's song was interrupted as Ma'ii came crashing through the cornfield. "I haven't seen you in a long while!" he exclaimed as he shook Horned Toad's entire body in a rough, coyote-style handshake. Then Ma'ii noticed the tall corn stalks. He could almost taste those plump, juicy, young ears of corn.

"Welcome to my — " Horned Toad started to say, but Ma'ii rudely interrupted him again, begging Horned Toad to share his corn with his poor, hungry, long-lost cousin.

Horned Toad knew he had work to do. But being the nice fellow he was, he scampered off into the cornfield. And back he came, with a sackful of corn.

After a meal of delicious roast corn and squash stew, Ma'ii sat back and rubbed his big, full stomach. He licked his lips and paws. "My, that was a good appetizer," he said. "And if you wouldn't mind, my dear cousin, I am ready for the main course."

Horned Toad was mad. He'd worked hard to grow all this food. But being the nice fellow he was, he just scampered back into the cornfield once again and returned a short while later with another sackful of corn.

As soon as the ears of corn were roasted, Ma'ii gobbled them down without so much as a thank-you.

Horned Toad grew madder by the moment. Before Ma'ii could ask him for any more food, Horned Toad wagged his finger and scolded, "Cousin, you certainly eat way too much. If you must eat again, you will work in my cornfield."

Ma'ii hated working more than anything. That was why he traveled from one cousin to the next — for food and a place to sleep. With great reluctance, Ma'ii began to pull weeds and water the cornfield. But then he decided to drink the rest of the water himself.

After Horned Toad was out of sight, Ma'ii lay down in the shade of a big cornstalk. He thought how wonderful it would be to own a farm like this. Why, he wouldn't have to travel. He would just sit there in the brush hut and roast corn all day long. As he thought, he sang a soft song.

"Hey nay ya ho ye'
Hey nay ya ho ye'
I've been blessed with a cornfield this day
I've stopped my running and begging this day
Mother Earth has provided me with
Endless food this day
For I am the child of Ye'ii
Hey nay ya ho ye'
Hey nay ya ho ye'
Sweet smell of roast corn will fill the air
And carry my prayer to Father Sun above
To bless me some more
For I am the child of Ye'ii
Hey nay ya ho ye' "

As he sang, he schemed of a way to trick his cousin out of his farm. Ma'ii had lots of tricks that he had learned on his journeys. So he decided to fake a pain in his mouth.

"Help, cousin!" screamed Ma'ii. "*Waa oooh! Wee ooh ooh!*"

Horned Toad dropped what he was doing and came running. "What has happened, cousin?" he asked.

"I have a piece of hard corn stuck between my teeth," Ma'ii moaned. "Way back there, and I can't get to it . . . if only you could just climb into my mouth, perhaps you could wiggle it free and save me from this terrible pain! *Owww waa oooh!*"

Well, Horned Toad didn't really want to climb into Ma'ii's mouth. But being the nice fellow he was, he climbed all the way inside anyway.

SNAP!

Ma'ii's mouth closed tight and, just as fast, he swallowed his small cousin.

Then Ma'ii looked around at Horned Toad's farm. It was all his.

That afternoon, Ma'ii had another big meal of roast corn and squash stew. Then he fell asleep with a big grin on his face. But his sleep was brief.

"*Shil na aash. Shil na aash . . .*"

A strange, faraway voice awakened Ma'ii. He rubbed his eyes and looked about. "Sounds like someone is saying, 'My cousin. My cousin,' " he said to himself. "It is probably just a dream. It happens like that sometimes after a big meal."

Ma'ii rolled over and went back to sleep. But no sooner was he asleep again than the faraway voice returned.

"*Shil na aash . . .*"

This time, Ma'ii jumped up and raced around the brush hut. "Show yourself! Who is it?" he yelled.

Ma'ii was a superstitious fellow. He didn't like to be frightened. But now he was sure that cousin Horned Toad's spirit had come to haunt him. *Yee yah!*

Ma'ii fled to the other side of the cornfield. There he found a safe spot under a big juniper tree, where he fell asleep again. But no sooner was he asleep than the faraway voice returned.

"*Shil na aash.* It is me, Horned Toad. I am in your stomach," came the voice from deep inside of Ma'ii.

"B-But . . ." sputtered Ma'ii. "I-I thought you were — "

"No cousin," said Horned Toad. "I am fine. It's nice and warm in here. All the food I need and more keeps coming down. And best of all, I don't have to pull weeds . . . . But I would like to pull out these sharp things that are poking me in the side."

"*Ouch!*" yelped Ma'ii. "Those are my ribs!"

"Ahhh," sighed Horned Toad. "I think I found home." And he stretched himself out in a nice, cozy spot.

"Listen," hissed Ma'ii. "You come out this instant, or I'll drown you out."

"Oh, please, don't do that," said Horned Toad. "Please don't drown me."

But Ma'ii ignored his cousin's plea. He ran down to the creek and drank until he could hold no more. Then he smiled. He was rid of Horned Toad now.

"Water's good down here," came the small voice inside of Ma'ii. "And thank you. The cornmeal was making me quite thirsty. Cornmeal does that, you know."

Ma'ii was getting mad. "Come out right now or I will burn you out!" he growled.

But Horned Toad just yawned. "And give up this good life in here? Oh, no, not me."

Now Ma'ii was so mad he ran to the fire and stood over it with all four legs spread apart. The flames licked his stomach and scorched his hair and skin.

"*Oow oow ouch!*" Ma'ii yelped.

"Many thanks, cousin," Horned toad called out. "Now I have a nice, warm bath and hot cornmeal!"

Ma'ii was the maddest yet. "Come out here right now or I will crush you!" screamed Ma'ii as he ran towards the edge of the canyon. Just as he was about to jump, he realized that this may not be a good idea.

"Listen, cousin," Ma'ii pleaded. "Come out now and we will settle this together."

"But I'm so comfortable in here," Horned Toad insisted. "I don't think I shall ever leave."

"Dear cousin, please. If you come out right now, you can have your farm back. I will leave at once and never bother you again."

"I would rather go exploring. After all, this is my new home," said Horned Toad.

Horned Toad's skin was too rough for Ma'ii's delicate insides. He swam through the tunnels and strange spaces inside of Ma'ii until he came upon Ma'ii's big, fat, thumping heart. Ma'ii screamed and begged for mercy.

Horned Toad gave Ma'ii's heart one big tug, then another. Ma'ii yelped and fell to the ground. He had fainted from fright.

Later that evening, Horned Toad crawled out through Ma'ii's mouth. Ma'ii was still out cold. Horned Toad took Ma'ii's big, greasy tongue and gave it a gigantic pull.

Ma'ii's eyes opened and he bolted to his feet. He let out a frightful scream and ran off into the dusk without ever looking back once.

And even to this day, Ma'ii leaves his cousin Horned Toad alone.

About the Coyote and the Horned Toad

Among the Navajo, Coyote has many names. In our stories of Coyote as trickster and mischief maker, we call him Ma'ii. He also has many faces. In some of our stories he is a hero. Sometimes he is a villain. In some stories he is brave and in others he is cowardly. *Ma'ii Jol Dlooshi'* or "Coyote out walking stories" are teaching tales. These stories show us proper ways to conduct ourselves. They also explain natural phenomena, but they are always pure entertainment.

Whenever we come upon a horned toad, we gently place it over our heart and greet it. "*Ya ateeh shi che*" ("Hello, my grandfather"). We believe it gives strength of heart and mind. We never harm our grandfather.

Glossary of Navajo Words

Word	Pronunciation	Translation
Ahéhee'	(A HYEH hay)	Thank you
Hágoónee'	(Ha go NAY)	Good-bye
Ma'ii	(Ma EEH)	Coyote
Shiɫ na aash	(Sheelsh na ash)	My cousin
Shi che	(Shee chay)	My grandfather
Yá'át'ééh	(YAH ah t eh)	A greeting, like hello
Yee yah!	(Yee yah)	An expression of fright
Ye'ii	(Yeh EEH)	Navajo diety (one of the most important ones)

In Response

What If? Write a new ending for the story. What would have happened if Horned Toad died when Ma'ii ate him? Would Ma'ii be able to take care of the farm by himself? Explain why or why not in your ending.

Be a Comic Artist Ma'ii, the coyote in "Ma'ii and Cousin Horned Toad" and Snake in "The Singing Snake" are alike in many ways. Imagine that they met and started talking about their adventures. What would they say? Would they warn each other? Would they brag? Draw a comic strip to tell what happens. Share your comic with classmates.

Coyote Song Look at Ma'ii's song on page 74. Use a drum or two sticks to beat out the time to the song. While you are beating the time, you or a partner can say the words.

Puppet Show With a partner, create puppets of Ma'ii and Horned Toad. Then choose a scene from the story or write your own. Perform the scene with your puppets.

Paul Bunyan and Babe

Paul Bunyan was a giant logger. He was huge, as big as a mountain, and very strong. He could clear a whole forest in a single morning.

Paul was pretty lonely being the only giant around. Then Paul met Babe. This is how it happened. One day while Paul was walking through the snow, he saw what he thought were mountains. As he got closer, he spotted a big white horn, then two,

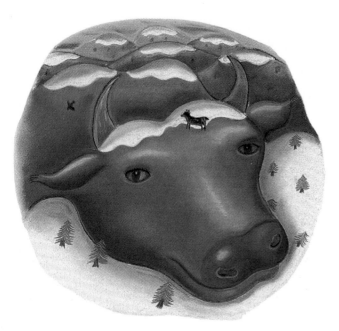

then eyes staring up at him. It was Babe, the blue ox, taking a nap in the snow. As soon as Babe saw Paul, up he jumped and licked Paul's nose. Right then, Paul decided Babe could be his friend. He didn't have to be lonely ever again.

One time, Paul set up a logging camp with two cooks, named Sourdough Sam and Biscuit Slim. There were many workers in the camp, and they all needed to eat. Paul made a griddle so big that it took up a whole acre of land. To get the griddle greased, the cooks tied slabs of bacon to the feet of some of the workers. Then the workers skated on the griddle until it was hot enough to cook the pancakes. The table where the men would eat was three miles long. This was too far for the waiters to walk.

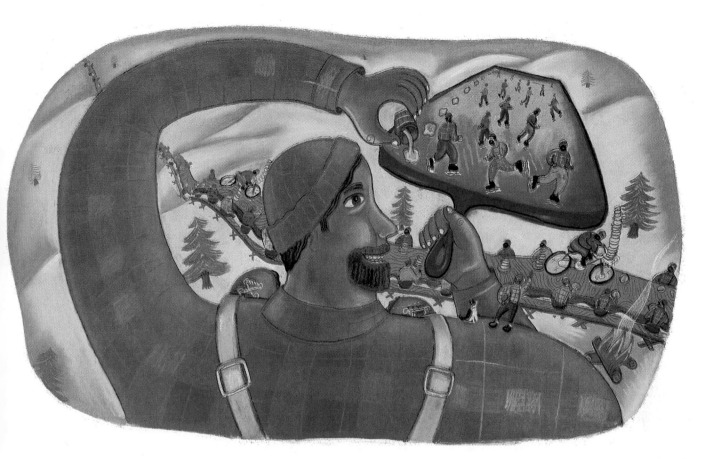

So they rode bicycles down the center of the table. On their way, they dropped off as many pancakes as each man could eat.

Paul and Babe traveled the country, clearing trees so that people could have farms. Wherever they went, people remembered them by telling stories about the amazing things they did. Together they had many adventures and remained best friends for the rest of their lives.

Author and Illustrator at Work

Rosalind C. Wang says that "writing, the same as playing ball or playing the piano, needs practice all the time." To improve your writing, Wang recommends keeping a journal and reading as much as possible. She believes that the world of books is "a big pot of treasure from which you can borrow freely and enjoy."

Shao Wei Liu was born in China, where she studied brush painting and calligraphy. Calligraphy is the art of fine handwriting. She went to college in China to become a scientist, but when she moved to the United States a few years later, she studied art. She feels she was born to be an artist and not a scientist. Liu says, "Art is something that will allow you to enjoy life. It is a way to express yourself."

THE MAGICAL STARFRUIT TREE

by Rosalind C. Wang

paintings by Shao Wei Liu

Long, long ago in the southern part of China, there lived a fruit peddler named Ah-Di. He was so mean and so greedy that no one liked him. Yet his starfruit always grew so ripe and juicy that people from faraway lands would come to buy them in the market.

One summer day, the fruit peddler packed his two big baskets full of luscious yellow starfruit and rushed to the market. A great crowd had gathered because it was the monthly market day. They came to shop and to watch the acrobats perform. Ah-Di set up his fruit stand near the performers, under a yum-yum tree, and was pleased with himself for finding such a good spot. He murmured, "The day is very hot and dry. People will be thirsty. I shall sell every one of my ripe and juicy starfruit and make lots of money!"

Some people could not afford to buy his starfruit and could only look longingly at them. Ah-Di was so mean and nasty. He would yell at the poor bystanders, "Are you going to buy? If not, stay away! Don't block my fortune!"

Toward afternoon, an old man came along and stopped in front of the fruit stand. His faded green clothes were shabby, and he didn't have a penny in his pocket. All he had in his hand was a tree branch that served as his cane. He wore a straw hat atop his head, and his wrinkled face was covered with sweat and dust. But if you looked closely, you could see there was something different about this old man. When the sun shone into his dark brown eyes, they sparkled with a mysterious jade-green color.

The old man observed Ah-Di's juicy starfruit and said, "Oh good Fruit Peddler, I am very thirsty, but I have no money to buy your fruit. I believe that you are a kind-hearted man. Surely you will have mercy on an old man and give me a juicy starfruit."

"Go away, old beggar!" the stingy Ah-Di shouted. "My starfruit are for *sale*. They bring me wealth. I do not give my fruit away to anyone!"

"Oh good Fruit Peddler, have mercy on these old bones. I do not want your biggest and plumpest starfruit. All I want is your smallest one, one that you might throw away. I know the Jade Emperor of Heaven will bless you for your kindness."

"Who do you think you are?" Ah-Di yelled. "Why do I need *you* to ask the Jade Emperor to give me blessings?" Go away before I beat you with my stick!"

People in the marketplace heard the noise and formed a circle around them.

"Shame on you, Fruit Peddler," said a bystander. "This old man is tired and thirsty. Give him a starfruit. It will not hurt you a bit, but a small fruit will quench his thirst. The Jade Emperor of Heaven will surely reward you for your kindness."

"That's right!" cried the crowd, "Have pity on the old man."

"Oh yes, saying is easier than doing!" yelled Ah-Di. "It is not *your* starfruit you give away so easily. You do not toil and labor to produce them! If you have such a kind heart, why don't you buy one and give it to this old beggar?"

At that moment, a young boy named Ming-Ming, one of the acrobats, had just finished his performance. He came forward with two copper coins and handed them to the stingy Ah-Di.

"I will buy a starfruit for the Lau Gong Gong (old grandpa)," said Ming-Ming. He then turned to the old man and said very kindly, "Lau Gong Gong, you may now select a large, juicy starfruit for yourself. Do not worry, I have paid the fruit peddler."

The old man hesitated, "How can I take your money? You have worked hard for these two coins."

"Lau Gong Gong, I do not have much, but I am willing to share what I have. I'll perform again, and most of these kind aunties and uncles will give me more money."

The old man selected a starfruit and ate it down to the core. He then carefully picked out one of the seeds and threw the rest of the core away.

"Ahhh, it is so good," he said as he smiled. "Thank you, little boy. You have been very kind to me. Now, please help me perform for our audience here."

The old man used his cane to dig a hole in the ground. In it, he placed the carefully selected seed and asked the boy to pack the earth over the seed with his two little feet.

"Now I need to water the seed. Can anyone here supply me with a pot of hot water?"

The crowd was puzzled by his request. It was such a hot day. The old man would kill the seed for sure!

"Are you sure you need *hot* water?" someone from the crowd exclaimed. People looked at each other, hoping someone would explain this peculiar logic. Some stood there quietly, while others shook their heads, thinking that the old man was simply light-headed from the heat. Finally, someone from the crowd handed over a pot of boiling water, which the old man sprinkled on the ground.

A tiny green shoot sprang up immediately. As the crowd watched in awe, the plant grew taller and taller and taller. Their eyes followed the plant as it grew, and their heads tilted back farther and farther and farther until they could no longer see the top. They did not know exactly when the plant stopped growing, but their necks were sore from looking up.

The old man pointed his cane at the tree and said, "Leaves, my good tree, grow leaves!" and the tree instantly became an umbrella of green leaves, shading the crowd from the scorching sun.

While the crowd stood there dumbfounded, the old man pointed his cane at the branches of the tree and said, "Bloom, my good tree, bloom!" and the tree burst forth pink and violet flowers.

The crowd gasped in amazement. No sooner had they uttered oohs and ahhhs of wonder, when once again, the old man pointed his cane at the tree and said, "Fruit, my good tree, bear sweet and juicy fruit!" A gentle breeze swept over the tree and blew the beautiful blossoms down upon the crowd. In place of the flowers, big, bright starfruit appeared on the branches.

By then, the news of this strange happening had spread quickly throughout the marketplace. Everyone, including Ah-Di, rushed over and gathered around the old man and his amazing tree.

After calming the restless crowd, the old man turned to Ming-Ming and said, "It is your turn to perform. Please use your nimble feet to climb up into the branches and gather the juicy starfruit for all of us."

Obediently, the boy climbed up the tree trunk like a little monkey. He picked the starfruit and passed them out to all the bystanders. Even the stingy peddler received his share. Ah-Di thought to himself, "Hmm . . . that's funny! This starfruit is as sweet and juicy as those in my baskets."

After everyone enjoyed their starfruit, the old man picked up his cane and struck the tree trunk several times. Each blow made the tree shrink smaller and smaller until it was the size of his palm. He then gave it to Ming-Ming and said, "Thank you for your assistance, little fellow. Plant this tree in your yard and you will have plenty of starfruit to quench your thirst every summer." Ming-Ming thanked him, and the old man picked up his cane, bowed to the audience, and walked through the crowd and down the dusty road.

Stunned by the series of strange happenings, people rubbed their eyes. They could hardly believe what they had seen. They even licked their lips to assure themselves that they had indeed eaten one of the sweet, juicy starfruit.

Suddenly, Ah-Di remembered his unattended fruit baskets. With all these people, he could still sell more fruit. But when he looked into the baskets, they were empty. His high-pitched scream filled the air.

"My starfruit! My starfruit!" cried the mean, stingy, Ah-Di. "All my starfruit are gone from my baskets! It must have been that wretched old man who took my fruit and gave them to the crowd. Oh! Oh! All my wealth is gone!"

Leaving his two empty baskets behind, Ah-Di ran down the dirt road as quickly as he could to look for the old man. But alas! The only thing he found was the tree branch that the old man used as a cane, lying alongside the road.

The crowd broke into laughter at the greedy Ah-Di.

"That old man must have been a messenger sent down by the Jade Emperor of Heaven to teach that mean fruit peddler a lesson," said one person.

"That stingy fruit peddler deserves this for the way he treated the old man," said another person.

Yes, yes, the crowd all nodded in agreement. The Jade Emperor of Heaven is wise and just. Those who do not have a kind heart and respect for the old will surely be punished. But those who care about others and share what they have will surely be rewarded.

In Response

What's Next? The old man gave the magical starfruit tree to Ming-Ming so the boy would always have starfruit to eat. Write a paragraph or two. Tell what might happen when Ming-Ming gets home and plants the tree in his yard.

Make a Face Create a mask of a favorite character. Make the mask using materials available in your classroom, like paper bags, boxes, and posterboard. Decorate your mask using crayons, paint, and scraps of fabric or yarn. Use your mask in retelling the story to younger children.

It Really Happened! Pretend that you were in the market and saw the magical starfruit tree, but when you went home, no one would believe your story. Role-play for your family the old man, Ming-Ming, the crowd, and the growing starfruit tree to show what happened.

Folk Tales and Art

These paintings are about folk heroes. Sinbad the Sailor, a character from an Arabian folk tale, had many adventures at sea. Paul Revere is a real person whose famous ride warned the colonists at the start of the American Revolution. What is alike and different about these paintings? How do they make you feel?

Sinbad the Sailor
painting by Paul Klee (Swiss), 1923

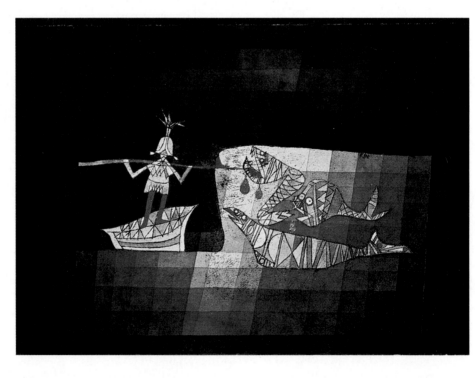

Midnight Ride of Paul Revere

painting by Grant Wood (U.S.), 1931

Star Boy

retold and illustrated by Paul Goble,
Macmillan, 1983

Long ago, Star Boy's mother made the Sun angry,
and she and Star Boy were sent to Earth to live.
Now Star Boy must return to the Sky World to
ask the Sun for his help.

The Cat's Purr

written and illustrated by Ashley Bryan,
Atheneum, 1985

Cat and Rat are best friends. When Cat gets a
special purring drum, Rat wants to play it, too,
and the friends soon become enemies.

The Name of the Tree

by Celia Barker Lottridge, illustrated by Ian
Wallace, Margaret K. McElderry Books, 1989

A group of starving animals finds a tree that will
only give fruit if the animals say its name. The
animals take turns asking Lion King the tree's
name. Which animal will remember the name?

Nessa's Story

by Nancy Luenn, illustrated by Neil Waldman,
Atheneum, 1994

All winter Nessa listens to stories her
grandmother tells. In summer, Nessa goes looking
for eggs for her grandmother and a story of her
own. Out on the tundra, Nessa finds an amazing
story.

The Boy and the Ghost

by Robert D. San Souci, illustrated by J. Brian
Pinkney, Simon and Schuster, 1989

On his way to find his fortune, Thomas shares his
meal with a poor man. In return, the stranger
tells Thomas about a hidden treasure in a
haunted mansion.

Taking Care of the Earth

GIUSTI

People began to understand, as never before, how much the river, the fishes, the otters, even the trees and birds had meant to the village.

— Alejandro Cruz Martinez
The Woman Who Outshone the Sun

Taking Care of the Earth

Contents

Books from Your Classroom Library

Never Kiss an Alligator! by Colleen Stanley Bare will tell you lots of things about how alligators survive in the wild.

The Year of the Panda by Miriam Schlein is a story about a Chinese boy who rescues a baby panda. In the process, he learns why pandas are endangered and how the government tries to help them.

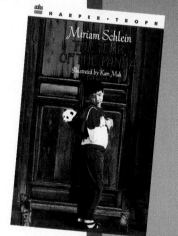

Geo Zone

Have you noticed the wild world around you? It needs help, wherever you are. From the water in your street to the toilet on Mount Everest, read all about it in the **Theme Magazine** *Geo Zone.*

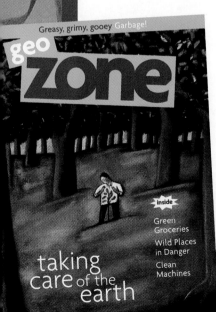

Author and Illustrator at Work

★ Award-winning Author and Illustrator

 Chris Van Allsburg says about his artwork, "I like to create a world . . . where strange things may happen." Van Allsburg's art has always been a little mysterious, which made it easy for him to illustrate Walter's dreams in *Just a Dream*.

People often ask Chris Van Allsburg where he gets his ideas. As a joke he says, "I steal them from the neighborhood kids" or "they are beamed to me from outer space." This is just his way of saying that he doesn't know where his ideas come from. His first ideas for a story are like clues that will lead him to a discovery—the finished book!

As usual, Walter stopped at the bakery on his way home from school. He bought one large jelly-filled doughnut. He took the pastry from its bag, eating quickly as he walked along. He licked the red jelly from his fingers. Then he crumpled up the empty bag and threw it at a fire hydrant.

At home Walter saw Rose, the little girl next door, watering a tree that had just been planted. "It's my birthday present," she said proudly.

Walter couldn't understand why anyone would want a tree for a present. His own birthday was just a few days away, "And I'm not getting some dumb plant," he told Rose.

After dinner Walter took out the trash. Three cans stood next to the garage. One was for bottles, one for cans, and one for everything else. As usual, Walter dumped everything into one can. He was too busy to sort through garbage, especially when there was something good on television.

The show that Walter was so eager to watch was about a boy who lived in the future. The boy flew around in a tiny airplane that he parked on the roof of his house. He had a robot and a small machine that could make any kind of food with the push of a button.

Walter went to bed wishing he lived in the future. He couldn't wait to have his own tiny plane, a robot to take out the trash, and a machine that could make jelly doughnuts by the thousands. When he fell asleep, his wish came true. That night Walter's bed traveled to . . .

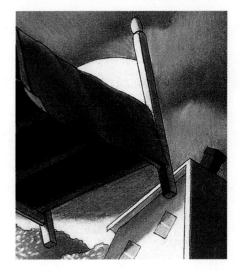

the future.

Walter woke up in the middle of a huge dump. A bulldozer was pushing a heap of bulging trash bags toward him. "Stop!" he yelled.

The man driving the bulldozer put his machine in neutral. "Oh, sorry," he said. "Didn't see you."

Walter looked at the distant mountains of trash and saw half-buried houses. "Do people live here?" he asked.

"Not anymore," answered the man.

A few feet from the bed was a rusty old street sign that read FLORAL AVENUE. "Oh no," gasped Walter. He lived on Floral Avenue.

The driver revved up his bulldozer. "Well," he shouted, "back to work!"

Walter pulled the covers over his head. This can't be the future, he thought. I'm sure it's just a dream. He went back to sleep.

But not for long . . .

Walter peered over the edge of his bed, which was caught in the branches of a tall tree. Down below, he could see two men carrying a large saw. "Hello!" Walter yelled out.

"Hello to you!" they shouted back.

"You aren't going to cut down this tree, are you?" Walter asked.

But the woodcutters didn't answer. They took off their jackets, rolled up their sleeves, and got to work. Back and forth they pushed the saw, slicing through the trunk of Walter's tree. "You must need this tree for something important," Walter called down.

"Oh yes," they said, "very important." Then Walter noticed lettering on the woodcutters' jackets. He could just make out the words: QUALITY TOOTHPICK COMPANY. Walter sighed and slid back under the blankets.

Until . . .

Walter couldn't stop coughing. His bed was balanced on the rim of a giant smokestack. The air was filled with smoke that burned his throat and made his eyes itch. All around him, dozens of smokestacks belched thick clouds of hot, foul smoke. A workman climbed one of the stacks.

"What is this place?" Walter called out.

"This is the Maximum Strength Medicine Factory," the man answered.

"Gosh," said Walter, looking at all the smoke, "what kind of medicine do they make here?"

"Wonderful medicine," the workman replied, "for burning throats and itching eyes."

Walter started coughing again.
"I can get you some," the
man offered.

"No thanks," said Walter.
He buried his head in his pillow
and, when his coughing stopped,
fell asleep.

But then . . .

Snowflakes fell on Walter. He was high in the mountains. A group of people wearing snowshoes and long fur coats hiked past his bed.

"Where are you going?" Walter asked.

"To the hotel," one of them replied.

Walter turned around and saw an enormous building. A sign on it read HOTEL EVEREST. "Is that a hotel," asked Walter, "on the top of Mount Everest?"

"Yes," said one of the hikers. "Isn't it beautiful?"

"Well," Walter began. But the group didn't wait for his answer. They waved goodbye and marched away. Walter stared at the flashing yellow sign, then crawled back beneath his sheets.

But there was more to see . . .

Walter's hand was wet and cold. When he opened his eyes, he found himself floating on the open sea, drifting toward a fishing boat. The men on the boat were laughing and dancing.

"Ship ahoy!" Walter shouted.

The fishermen waved to him.

"What's the celebration for?" he asked.

"We've just caught a fish," one of them yelled back. "Our second one this week!" They held up their small fish for Walter to see.

"Aren't you supposed to throw the little ones back? Walter asked.

But the fishermen didn't hear him. They were busy singing and dancing.

Walter turned away. Soon the
rocking of the bed put him to sleep.

But only for a moment . . .

A loud, shrieking horn nearly lifted Walter off his mattress. He jumped up. There were cars and trucks all around him, horns honking loudly, creeping along inch by inch. Every driver had a car phone in one hand and a big cup of coffee in the other.

When the traffic stopped completely, the honking grew even louder. Walter could not get back to sleep.

Hours passed, and he wondered if he'd be stuck on this highway forever. He pulled his pillow tightly around his head. This can't be the future, he thought.

Where are the tiny airplanes, the robots? The honking continued into the night, until finally, one by one, the cars became quiet as their drivers, and Walter, went to sleep.

But his bed traveled on . . .

Walter looked up. A horse stood right over his bed, staring directly at him. In the saddle was a woman wearing cowboy clothes. "My horse likes you," she said.

"Good," replied Walter, who wondered where he'd ended up this time. All he could see was a dull yellow haze.

"Son," the woman told him, spreading her arms in front of her, "this is the mighty Grand Canyon."

Walter gazed into the foggy distance.

"Of course," she went on, "with all this smog, nobody's gotten a good look at it for years."

The woman offered to sell Walter some postcards that showed the canyon in the old days. "They're real pretty," she said.

But he couldn't look. It's just a dream, he told himself. I know I'll wake up soon, back in my room.

But he didn't . . .

Walter looked out from under his sheets. His bed was flying through the night sky. A flock of ducks passed overhead. One of them landed on the bed, and to Walter's surprise, he began to speak. "I hope you don't mind," the bird said, "if I take a short rest here." The ducks had been flying for days looking for the pond where they had always stopped to eat.

"I'm sure it's down there somewhere," Walter said, though he suspected something awful might have happened. After a while the duck waddled to the edge of the bed, took a deep breath, and flew off. "Good luck," Walter called

to him. Then he pulled the blanket over his head. "It's just a dream," he whispered, and wondered if it would ever end.

Then finally . . .

Walter's bed returned to the present. He was safe in his room again, but he felt terrible. The future he'd seen was not what he'd expected. Robots and little airplanes didn't seem very important now. He looked out his window at the trees and lawns in the early morning light, then jumped out of bed.

He ran outside and down the block, still in his pajamas. He found the empty jelly doughnut bag he'd thrown at the fire hydrant the day before. Then Walter went back home and, before the sun came up, sorted all the trash by the garage.

A few days later, on Walter's birthday, all his friends came over

for cake and ice cream. They loved his new toys: the laser gun set, electric yo-yo, and inflatable dinosaurs. "My best present," Walter told them, "is outside." Then he showed them the gift that he'd picked out that morning—a tree.

After the party, Walter and his dad planted the birthday present.

When he went to bed, Walter looked out his window. He could see his tree and the tree Rose had planted on her birthday. He liked the way they looked, side by side. Then he went to sleep, but not for long, because that night Walter's bed took him away again.

When Walter woke up, his bed was standing in the shade of the two tall trees. The sky was blue. Laundry hanging from a clothesline flapped in the breeze. A man pushed an old motorless lawn mower. This isn't the future, Walter thought. It's the past.

"Good morning," the man said. "You've found a nice place to sleep."

"Yes, I have," Walter agreed.

There was something very peaceful about the huge trees next to his bed.

The man looked up at the rustling leaves. "My great-grandmother planted one of these trees," he said, "when she was a little girl."

Walter looked up at the leaves too, and realized where his bed had taken him. This was the future, after all, a different kind of future.

There were still no robots or tiny airplanes. There weren't even any clothes dryers or gas-powered lawn mowers. Walter lay back and smiled. "I like it here," he told the man, then drifted off to sleep in the shade of the two giant trees—the trees he and Rose had planted so many years ago.

In Response

Taking Care of the Trees
Suppose Walter went out to water his tree at the same time Rose was watering hers. What might they say to each other? Who would speak first? Write down what they say.

Get Unreal! In this story, you saw a real, everyday object—Walter's bed—in unreal settings. Choose an everyday object, such as your own bed, a bicycle, or a chair, and draw a picture of it in an unreal setting.

Dream Team Gather in small groups to act out one of Walter's dreams. Each group member should have a part. Some students can make sound effects, for example, the sound of wind on Mount Everest.

acorn

by Valerie Worth

An acorn
Fits perfectly
Into its shingled
Cup, with a stick
Attached
At the top,

Its polished
Nut curves
In the shape
Of a drop, drawn
Down to a thorn
At the tip,

And its heart
Holds folded
Thick white fat
From which
A marvelous
Tree grows up:

I think no better
Invention or
Mechanical trick
Could ever
Be bought
In a shop.

Author and Illustrator at Work

★ Award-winning Author

Melvin Berger has written more than one hundred books, which have been translated into fifteen different languages. Most of Berger's books are about science, but he also likes to write about music because he used to be a high-school music teacher. Berger has a collection of antique microscopes and other old scientific instruments.

★ Award-winning Illustrator

Paul Mirocha always wanted to combine art and science. He found a way to do just that by studying scientific illustration. Mirocha and his family live near Tucson, Arizona, in the Sonoran Desert. Mirocha loves learning about the desert and drawing the plants and animals that live there. In his drawings, Mirocha tries to show how nature and humans affect each other.

THE NIGHT OF MARCH 24, 1989, was dark and cold. A huge, black oil tanker glided out of the port of Valdez, Alaska. Painted on its bow was its name — *Exxon Valdez*.

The *Exxon Valdez* floated low in the water. About fifty million gallons of crude oil weighed it down.

The huge tanker slowly sailed out into Prince William Sound. And then, suddenly, it happened.

CRUNCH!

The ship slammed into an underwater reef!

Thick, black oil flowed out of the *Exxon Valdez*'s smashed tanks. It poured into the dark water.

The *Exxon Valdez* spilled out 11 million gallons of oil. That much oil could fill over 1,000 big swimming pools.

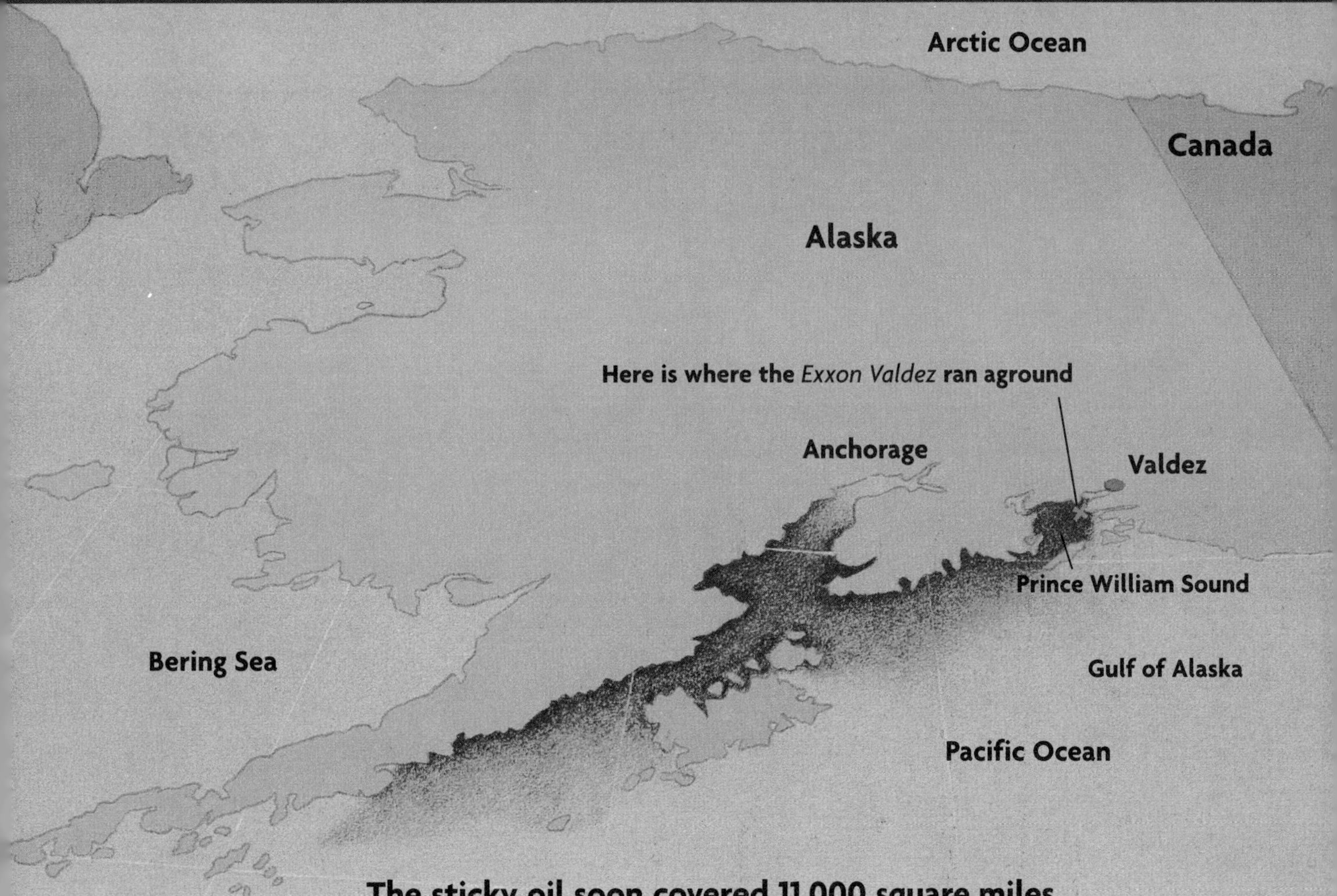

Arctic Ocean

Canada

Alaska

Here is where the *Exxon Valdez* **ran aground**

Anchorage

Valdez

Prince William Sound

Bering Sea

Gulf of Alaska

Pacific Ocean

The sticky oil soon covered 11,000 square miles of ocean water. That is an area as big as the state of Maryland.

It damaged about 1,250 miles of Alaska's coastline. That is longer than the entire Atlantic Coast of the United States.

The oil stuck to the feathers of many ducks, geese, and other seabirds. The birds couldn't swim or fly. Over 300,000 died.

Oil got into the bodies of fish, shrimp, and crabs. No one knows how many of them were killed.

People of all ages volunteered to help in the clean-up of the oil spill.

164

Sea otters, sea lions, harbor seals, and killer whales swallowed oil. They breathed the poisonous fumes. Their bodies were coated with oil. Thousands of these marine mammals died.

The spill from the *Exxon Valdez* was one of the worst in our country's history. But it was not the only one. An oil spill occurs somewhere in the world almost every day of the year.

Oil spills have many causes. Some are accidents.

- A tanker like the *Exxon Valdez* runs aground or collides with another ship.
- Workers make mistakes as a tanker is being loaded or unloaded.
- An undersea oil well starts to leak.
- A tank or a pipe breaks at a shore oil terminal.

Some oil spills occur on purpose. The tanker captain tells the workers to clean out the tanks. Sometimes they flush the old oil into the sea.

Tanker collides with another tanker

Undersea oil well starts to leak

Pipe breaks at shore oil terminal

The causes of oil spills differ. But the result is the same. The oil spreads out. It floats on top of the water.

Experts on oil spills rush to the scene. They start to clean up the mess.

Their first job is to stop the oil from spreading. They put a boom around the spill. The boom is like a collar. It keeps the oil in one place.

For small spills, the experts may call for a skimmer. There are several kinds of skimmers. One type works like a giant vacuum cleaner. It sucks up the oil from the water. Sometimes the oil the skimmer collects can be used again.

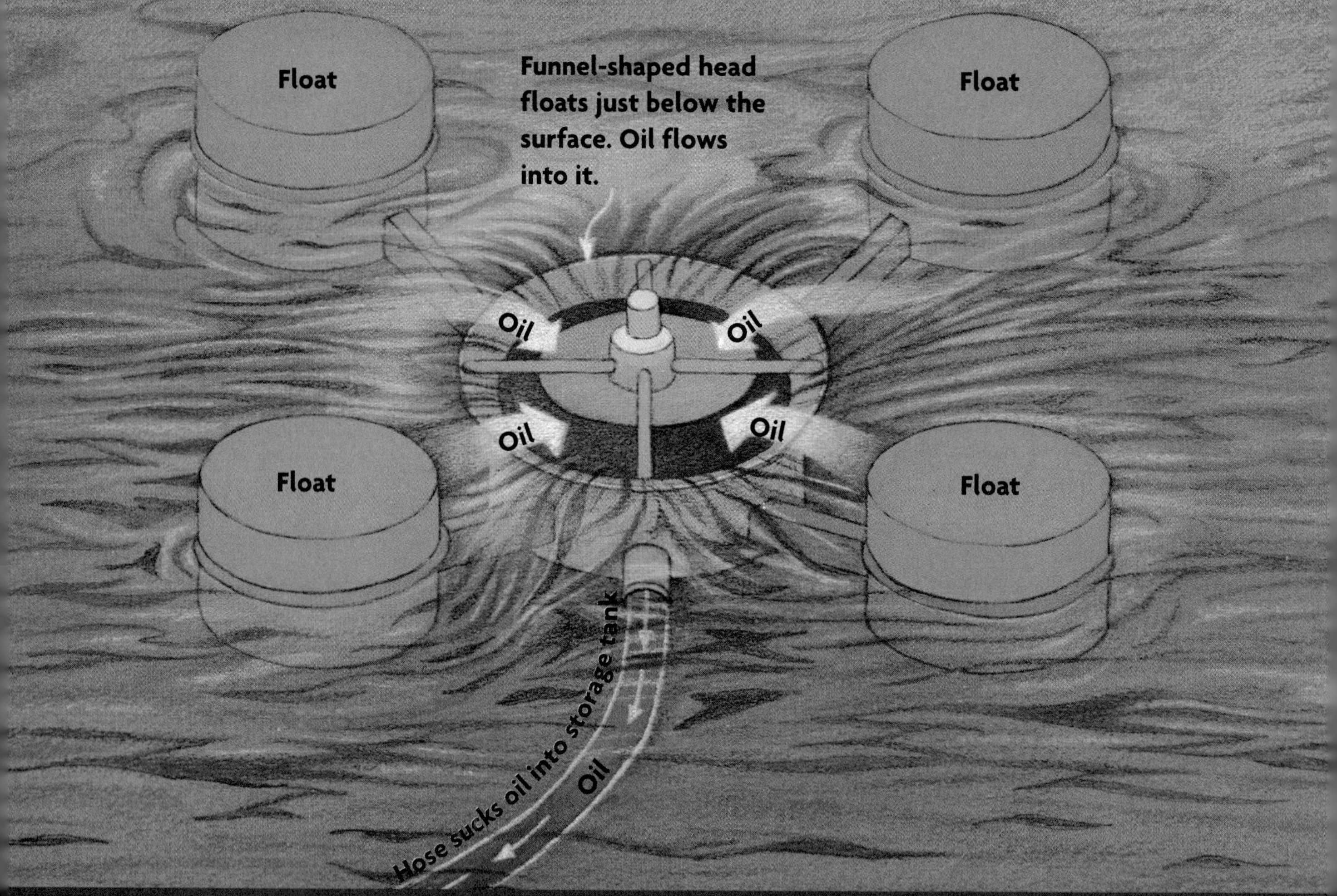

Float

Float

Funnel-shaped head floats just below the surface. Oil flows into it.

Oil

Oil

Oil

Oil

Float

Float

Hose sucks oil into storage tank

Oil

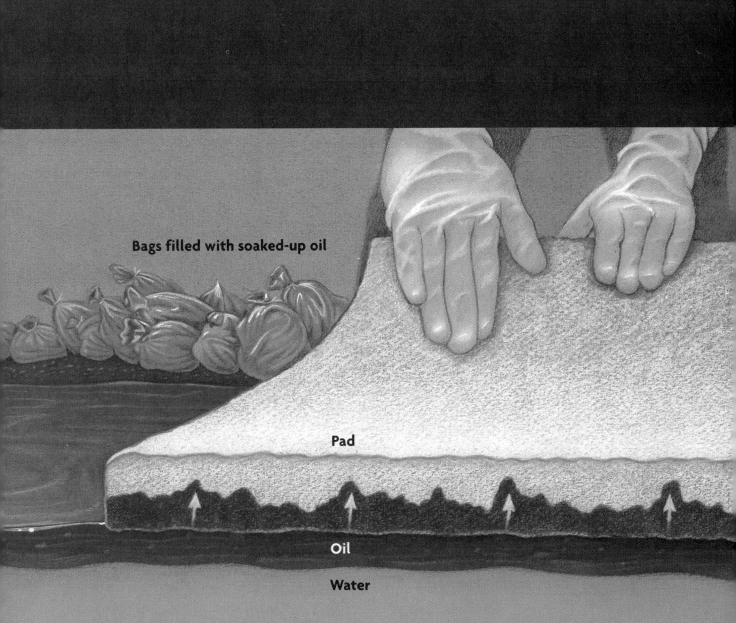

Bags filled with soaked-up oil

Pad

Oil

Water

For some small spills, experts place special pads on top of the oil. The pads are like sponges. They soak up the oil. Then they have to get rid of the soaked-up oil.

For larger spills, the experts may set the oil on fire. But the fire sends smoke and gas into the air and leaves ash in the water.

Cleanup crews also use chemicals to get rid of large oil spills. People aboard planes or boats spread the chemicals on the oil.

Some chemicals break the oil into tiny bits. The tiny bits mix with the water.

Other chemicals make the oil come together. The oil forms a layer like a sheet of rubber. One type of skimmer lifts the "sheet" of oil and oily debris out of the water.

Chemicals make the oil less harmful. But they add poisons to the water.

In time, the oil from most spills drifts up onto the shore. Scientists spray the rocks and sand with hot water to wash the oil back into the sea. But the hot spray may also push the oil farther into the rocks and sand. Here the oil can harm plants and animals that live on the shore.

Scientists sometimes add bacteria to the oil along the shore. The bacteria "eat" the oil and change it into harmless substances. But it would take huge amounts of bacteria to get rid of a big oil spill.

Sometimes the experts decide that no action is the best way to treat an oil spill. The wind and waves mix the oil and water together. It is like mixing oil and vinegar to make salad dressing. In time, much of the oil disappears.

Oil spills are major disasters. Slowly scientists are learning how to clean them up. They are learning how to prevent spills. How can we help to prevent oil spills, too?

How to Help Prevent Oil Spills

We can use less oil. If we use less oil, there will be fewer oil tankers in the oceans. Then the chance of oil spills will not be as great.

One way to save oil is to use less electricity. Electricity is often produced by burning oil. Less electricity means less oil.

Another way to cut oil needs is to use less gasoline, which is made from oil. That means driving smaller cars and staying within the speed limit.

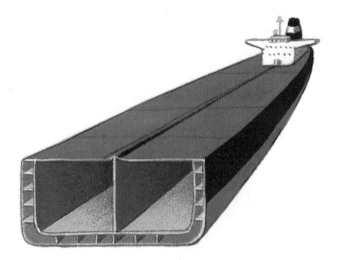

We also can write letters to members of Congress. Tell them we want new laws to prevent oil spills:

- Oil tankers should have double hulls. If the outer hull is damaged, the inner one will still hold the oil.

- Booms, skimmers, chemicals, and bacteria should be kept ready for emergencies all around the world.
- Oil companies should be helped to find new oil fields in the United States. They should not just depend on oil shipped from abroad.

- Tankers should have the most modern radar, radio, and other safety systems. This will help to prevent collisions.
- Experts should teach tanker crews how to handle oil spills.

Together we can make our seas and shorelines clean and beautiful again!

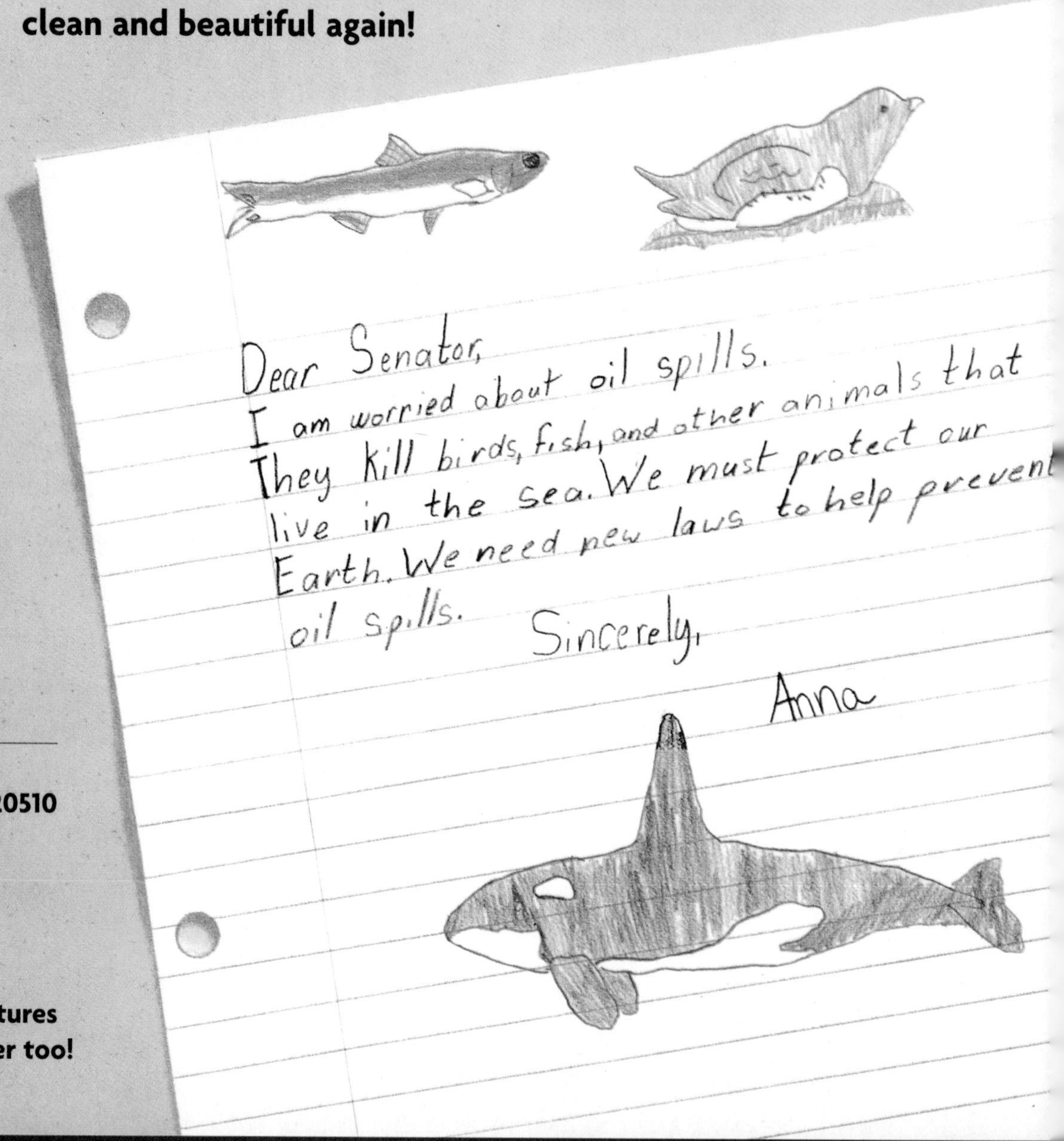

Dear Senator,
I am worried about oil spills.
They kill birds, fish, and other animals that live in the sea. We must protect our Earth. We need new laws to help prevent oil spills.

Sincerely,

Anna

Senator _____
U.S. Senate
Washington, DC 20510

You can draw pictures in your letter later too!

IN RESPONSE

Draw an Oil Spill Imagine that there has been an oil spill near your home. First, draw a picture showing the spill at its worst. Then draw the same spill in the same place, but this time show people trying to clean things up. Write captions that tell what each person is doing.

Dear Friend Make believe that you are one of the animals caught in an oil spill. Write a letter to your best animal friend telling him or her what happened to you. Draw pictures on the letter if you wish.

Clean Up Your Act! With four or five of your classmates, plan and perform for the class a short play about an oil spill. You may want to begin by having a narrator explain what is going to happen.

Dear World

To everyone in the world

Because people throw rubbish away, animals suffer. As we let detergents flow into rivers, fish and other animals can't live in them. If we stopped doing this, there would be more places for us to enjoy ourselves and more room for us to live. Our lives would improve. Once I found a fish with crooked bones among the fish I caught and this made me realize that the river was polluted. I want the world to become a nice place to live in for animals and living things and people.

釘宮聡

Satoshi Kugimiya, age 11
Hiroshima, Japan

行成浄 12才
Hiroshi Yukinari, age 12, Hiroshima, Japan

Natasha Manayenkova, age 10
Omsk, Siberia

Dear people of the whole world,
take care of nature.

I like to swim but most of all I like watching
the sunset. The sky is flooded with pink
light. And the factories, as if out of spite, are
puffing away and the dirty smoke drifts in
the pink sky. And I want to shout for all the
world to hear: 'Do not pollute the air.'
I nearly cry. And at night when it's dark and
the factories are quiet I look at the stars.
I am filled with freedom and happiness. And
at that moment only my cat understands me.
We sit and gaze at the beautiful sky.

Your friend, a friend of nature:

Natasha Manayenkova, age 10
Omsk, Siberia

The Beauty of the Earth

The beauty of the earth has always made artists want to paint it. How are these three paintings alike? How are they different? How would *you* paint a scene that shows the beauty of the earth?

Harbor Under the Midnight Sun
Painting by William H. Johnson (U.S.), 1937

Hills and Mesa to the West
Painting by Georgia O'Keeffe (U.S.), 1945

The Yosemite Valley
Painting by
Albert Bierstadt
(U.S.), 1868

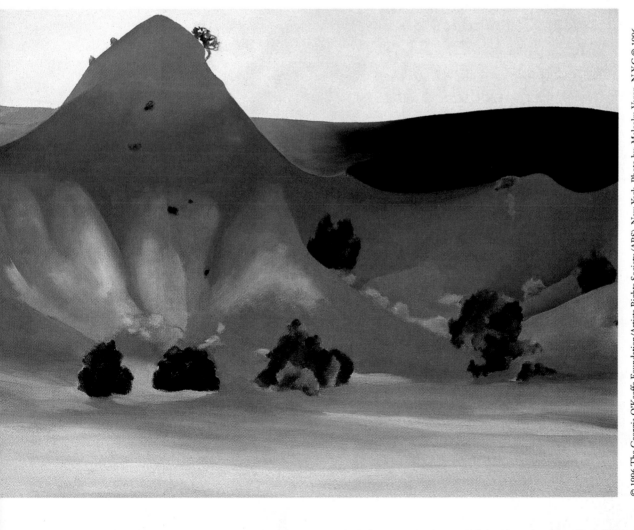

Author and Illustrator at Work

Alejandro Cruz Martinez was a Zapotec (*ZAH poh tehk*) Indian from Mexico. He spent years collecting the poems and stories of his people. The tale of Lucia Zenteno is a Zapotec legend that he recorded.

 Fernando Olivera first heard the legend of Lucia Zenteno from his close friend Alejandro Cruz Martinez. After Martinez died, Olivera painted many pictures of Lucia Zenteno. Perhaps the paintings were a way to remember his friendship with Martinez.

★ Award-winning Book

THE WOMAN WHO OUTSHONE THE SUN

La mujer que brillaba aún más que el sol

From a poem by
Alejandro Cruz Martinez

Pictures by
Fernando Olivera

The day Lucia Zenteno arrived, everyone in the village was astonished. No one knew where she came from. Yet they all saw that she was amazingly beautiful, and that she brought thousands of dancing butterflies and brightly-colored flowers on her skirts. She walked softly yet with quiet dignity, her long, unbraided hair flowing behind her. A loyal iguana walked at her side.

El día que llegó Lucía Zenteno al pueblo, todo el mundo se quedó asombrado. Nadie sabía de dónde venía esa mujer tan hermosa, que traía miles de mariposas y una infinidad de flores en su enagua, que caminaba suavemente y a la vez bien erguida, con su magnífica cabellera destrenzada ondeando libremente en el aire. A su lado la acompañaba una fiel iguana.

No one knew who she was, but they did know that nothing shone as brightly as Lucia Zenteno. Some people said that Lucia Zenteno outshone the sun. Others said that her glorious hair seemed to block out the light.

Everyone felt a little afraid of someone so wonderful and yet so strange.

Nadie sabía quién era, pero sí sabían que no había nada que brillara tanto como Lucía Zenteno. Alguna gente decía que Lucía Zenteno brillaba aún más que el sol. Otros decían que su espléndida cabellera parecía atajar la luz.

Todos comenzaron a sentir algo de miedo de este ser tan maravilloso y tan desconocido.

There used to be a river that ran by the town, almost the same river that runs by there now. And people said that when Lucia Zenteno went there to bathe, the river fell in love with her. The water rose from its bed and began to flow through her shining black hair.

When Lucia finished bathing, she would sit by the river and comb out her hair with a comb made from the wood of the mesquite tree. And when she did, the water, the fishes, and the otters would flow out of her hair and return to the river once more.

Cerca del pueblo había un río, casi el mismo que corre allí ahora y la gente decía que cuando Lucía Zenteno se fue a bañar al río, el río se enamoró de ella. El agua se salío de su cauce y comenzó a fluir suavemente por los negros cabellos du Lucía.

Cuando Lucía terminaba de bañarse, se sentaba al lado del río y se peinaba los cabellos con un peine de madera de mesquite. Y entonces las aguas, los peces y las nutrias se escurrían de la cabellera de Lucía Zenteno, y retornaban otra vez a formar parte del rio.

The old people of the village said that although Lucia was different from them, she should be honored and treated with respect. She understood the ways of nature, they said.

But some people did not listen to the elders. They were afraid of Lucia's powers, which they did not understand. And so they refused to answer Lucia's greetings, or offer their friendship. They called her cruel names and spied on her day and night.

Lucia did not return the meanness of the people. She kept to herself and continued to walk with her head held high.

Her quiet dignity angered some of the people. They whispered that Lucia must be trying to harm them. People became more afraid of Lucia and so they treated her more cruelly. Finally, they drove her from the village.

Los ancianos del pueblo decían que, aunque Lucía era distinta, habia que honrarla y guardarle respeto. Decían que ella tenía mucha afinidad con la naturaleza.

Pero alguna de la gente no siguió el consejo de los ancianos. Les tenían miedo a los poderes de Lucía, porque no los comprendían. Así que no le devolvían el saludo, ni le ofrecían su amistad. En cambio, hablaban mal de ella, y la espiaban día y noche.

Pero Lucía no los trataba a ellos de la misma manera. En cambio, se apartaba de ellos, y seguía caminando con dignidad.

Mucha de la gente se enojó a causa de esto. Comenzaron a murmurar que Lucía les iba a hacer daño a todos. Las gentes comenzaron a cogerle más temor, y al fin la obligaron a irse del pueblo.

Lucia went down to the river one last time to say good-bye. As always, the water rose to greet her and began to flow through her glorious hair. But this time when she tried to comb the river out of her hair, the river would not leave her.

And so, when Lucia Zenteno left the village, the river and the fishes and the otters went with her, leaving only a dry, winding riverbed, a serpent of sand where the water had been.

Everyone saw that Lucia Zenteno was leaving and that the river, the fishes, and the otters were leaving with her. The people were filled with despair. They had never imagined that their beautiful river would ever leave them, no matter what they did.

Lucía bajó al río una última vez para despedirse. Como siempre, las aguas salieron a saludarla y comenzaron a fluir entre sus largos cabellos. Pero esta vez, cuando Lucía trató de peinarse, el río no quiso separarse de ella.

Y por eso fue que cuando Lucía Zenteno se marchó del pueblo, el río, los peces y las nutrias se fueron con ella, dejando sólo una culebrita de arena por donde antes había corrido el río.

Todos vieron que Lucía se iba y que el río, los peces y las nutrias se iban con ella. La gente quedó desesperada. Nunca habían pensado que, hicieran lo que hicieran, su bello río los fuera a abandonar.

196

Where once there had been green trees and cool breezes, now no more rain fell, no birds sang, no otters played. The people and their animals suffered from thirst. People began to understand, as never before, how much the river, the fishes, the otters, even the trees and birds had meant to the village. They began to understand how much the river had loved Lucia Zenteno.

Donde antes había verdor y frescura, ahora ya no caía mas la lluvia, ni cantaban los pájaros, ni jugaban las nutrias. Los árboles perdieron sus hojas, y las plantas se secaron. La gente y los animales padecían de sed. Todos comenzaron a darse más cuenta que nunca de la importancia del río, de los peces, de las nutrias y aún de los árboles y de los pájaros para el pueblo. También comenzaron a darse cuenta de cuanto el río había querido a Lucía Zenteno.

The elders said that everyone must search for Lucia and beg her forgiveness. Some people did not want to. They were too afraid. But when the drought continued, everyone finally agreed to follow the elders' advice. And so the whole village set out in search of Lucia.

Los ancianos dijeron que todos debían ir en busca de Lucía a pedirle perdón. Pero algunas de las gentes no querían. Todavía temían a Lucía. Mas como el pueblo seguía sufriendo, al fin todos se pusieron de acuerdo. Siguiendo el consejo de los ancianos, fueron en busca de Lucía.

After many days of walking, the people found the iguana cave where Lucia had gone to seek refuge. Lucia was waiting for them, but they could not see her face. She had turned her back to the people.

At first no one dared say a word. Then two children called out, "Lucia, we have come to ask your forgiveness. Please have mercy on us and return our river!"

Tras mucha marcha, la gente encontró la cueva de iguana donde Lucía se había refugiado. Lucía los estaba esperando, pero no le podían ver la cara. Les había dado la espalda a la gente.

Al principio, nadie se atrevió a decir palabra. Luego, dos de los niños le suplicaron:—Lucía, hemos venido a pedirte perdón. Ten piedad de nosotros, te lo rogamos, y devuélvenos el río.

Lucia Zenteno turned and looked at the people. She saw their frightened tired faces, and she felt compassion for them. At last she spoke. "I will ask the river to return to you," she said. "But just as the river gives water to all who are thirsty, no matter who they are, so you must learn to treat everyone with kindness, even those who seem different from you."

The people remembered how they had treated Lucia, and they hung their heads in shame.

Lucía Zenteno se volvió a mirarlos. Vió sus caras llenas de miedo y de cansancio, y se compadeció de ellos. Al fin habló. —Le pediré al río que regrese con ustedes—les dijo—. Pero así como el río le da agua a todo el que está sediento, sin importarle quién sea, ustedes necesitan aprender a tratar a todos con bondad, aún a los que parecen ser distintos.

La gente recordó cómo habían tratado a Lucía y bajaron la cabeza, avergonzados.

Seeing that the people were truly sorry for what they had done, Lucia returned with them to the village and began to comb out her hair. She combed out the water, she combed out the fishes, she combed out the otters, and she kept on combing until the river had returned once more to where it belonged.

Al ver que la gente estaba verdaderamente arrepentida, Lucía regresó con ellos al pueblo y comenzó a peinarse los cabellos. Se peinó y se peinó, hasta que salieron las aguas, los peces y las nutria, y siguió peinándose hasta que todo el río había vuelto otra vez a su lugar.

The people were overjoyed to have their river again. They poured water over themselves and over their animals, they jumped into the river, and they laughed and cried with happiness.

In all the excitement, no one noticed at first that Lucia had disappeared again. When the children asked the elders where she had gone, the elders replied that Lucia had not really left them. Though they would not be able to see her, she would always be there, guiding and protecting them, helping them to live with love and understanding in their hearts.

La genta estaba feliz de tener al río de vuelta. Se echaban agua a si mismos y se la echaban a sus animales, se tiraban al río, y lloraban y reían de alegría.

Hubo tanta algarabía que nadie se dió cuenta de que Lucía había desaparecido de nuevo. Cuando los niños y las niñas le preguntaron a los ancianos a dónde se había ido, los ancianos dijeron que no los había abandonado. Aunque no la pudieran ver más, siempre estaría con ellos, cuidándolos y protegiéndolos. Siempre estaría ayudándolos a vivir de corazón, con amor y comprensión para todos.

In Response

How Would You Feel? Imagine that you are one of the characters in the story, perhaps Lucia Zenteno, her iguana, or one of the village children. Choose a scene from the story and write a poem that tells about your character's feelings at that time.

Put On a Puppet Play With some of your classmates, plan and perform a puppet play about Lucia Zenteno. Act out a scene from the story, using your own words. What will your characters say to each other?

Make a Cave Drawing Lucia and her iguana went to stay in the iguana cave. Imagine what the inside of their cave looked like. What things do you think Lucia would want inside the cave? Draw your ideas of what the cave would look like.

AND MY HEART SOARS

The beauty of the trees,
The softness of the air,
The fragrance of the grass,
  speaks to me.

The summit of the mountain,
The thunder of the sky,
The rhythm of the sea,
  speaks to me.

The faintness of the stars,
The freshness of the morning,
The dew drop on the flower,
  speaks to me.

The strength of fire,
The taste of salmon,
The trail of the sun,
and the life that never
goes away,
  They speak to me.

And my heart soars.

Chief Dan George

The Silver Bookcase

A Possible Tree
by Josephine Haskell Aldridge, illustrated by Daniel San Souci, Macmillan, 1993

A crooked old fir tree keeps the forest animals safe from harm within its branches. When Joe and his family see it on a moonlit winter night, they realize it's a special tree.

Turtle Watch
by George Ancona, photographs by the author, Macmillan, 1987

This book tells about the work of oceanographers in Brazil who are trying to save the endangered sea turtles. They are helped by two children who dig for turtle eggs and watch them hatch.

Amazon Boy
written and illustrated by Ted Lewin, Macmillan, 1993

Paulo, who lives deep in the Amazon jungle, takes an exciting trip down the river with his father and sees the wonderful gifts of the river at the busy Belem market.

Frog Odyssey

by **Juliet and Charles Snape,**
Simon & Schuster, 1991
When construction machines clog their pond, a band of frogs must make a dangerous journey through the city to find a new home.

A Tree in a Forest

by **Jan Thornhill,**
Simon & Schuster, 1991
Follow the life story of a majestic maple tree from its beginning as a tiny seedling in the forest.

Meeting Challenges

If you will tell me why
the fen appears impassable,
I then will tell you why
I think that I can get
across it if I try.

"I May, I Might, I Must"
by Marianne Moore

Contents

Books from Your Classroom Library

I Speak English for My Mom by Muriel Stanek is a story about Lupe, a young Mexican American, who must translate for her Spanish-speaking mother.

Much Ado About Aldo by Johanna Hurwitz tells the story of a boy whose love for the classroom crickets makes him want to give up eating meat.

Goal Zone

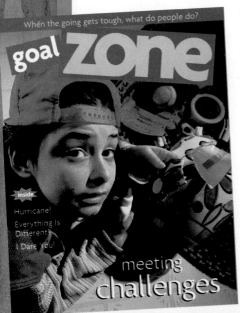

What's the biggest challenge you've had to face? Cold weather? Helping others? Moving to a new home? Living through a hurricane? People—and animals—meet challenges of all kinds in the Theme Magazine Goal Zone.

Author and Illustrator at Work

Trish Marx has made several visits to the zoo in Budapest, Hungary, the setting for *Hanna's Cold Winter*. Once she visited the zoo when the hippo house was closed for cleaning. She and her family were very disappointed because it was their last day in Budapest. Then a kind zookeeper invited them inside to see the hippos get their food and water. Marx hopes that you will be inspired by the true story of *Hanna's Cold Winter*.

★ Award-winning Illustrator

Barbara Knutson grew up in South Africa and now lives in Lima, Peru. She is an author as well as an illustrator and has written three books of African folk tales. Knutson enjoys traveling to schools to give talks about her experiences as a writer and an artist. She also teaches children how to create their own books and write their own folk tales.

Hanna's Cold Winter

written by
TRISH MARX

illustrations by
BARBARA KNUTSON

When I was a child, Sunday was my favorite day. Papa would wake up rested, after working all week at the paprika mill outside of town. For six days, summer and winter, he would pull heavy bags of dried peppers off the farmers' carts and haul them into the gaping mouth of the paprika factory, where they were ground into a fine spice. Papa used to say that the mouth of that factory was the only thing that was harder to feed than the mouths of his three children.

But that was on the six days during the week. On the seventh day, on Sunday, Papa could sleep until the sun woke him up. We would wait for him to come into the kitchen, dressed in his suit and his red bow tie and the gold cufflinks his grandfather had given to him when he got married.

"Well, well," he would say, trying to look stern.
"I suppose I shall have no peace today. I suppose I
shall have to wait to sit by the fire and drink your
mother's good coffee. Your faces tell me you want to
go out today."

We had been holding our breath, hoping Papa would say that. We had traveled all over Budapest, and sometimes to villages in the country, on these Sunday outings with Papa and Mama, and each of us had a special statue or building or park. I loved the carved stone lions guarding the bridge over the Danube River. My sister begged to go to the baths at the Gellert Hotel, and see the painted tiles, and feel the steam rising from the water that bubbled up from the ground.

My older brother, Gabor, who had pocket money, would run across the street from the baths to the market, where the farmers brought their eggs and tomatoes and chickens. He would soon be lost in the maze of cheese stalls and spice counters, but he always came out with candy for us all.

There was one place that was a favorite for all of us, but we never asked Papa to take us there because it cost money. We knew that when there were extra forints after buying Mama's sugar and butter, and the cloth for new pants, and new shoes for whichever one of us had grown too much, Papa would stand in the kitchen, and put his hand in his pocket, and jingle his coins, and smile a big smile. Then we knew it was a zoo Sunday.

The zoo in our town was down a big hill
and across the river from where we lived.
Papa would lift Eva onto his shoulders and
clasp my hand in his, and with Gabor
running ahead, we would walk down the hill
and over the river into the city of Pest.

Coming home, we could take the cog train that groaned its way up the hill, but going down was a game of chase, of hide-and-seek, and, always, of Papa's riddles.

"Little Tibor," he would ask me, "Those favorite lions of yours on the Lanchid bridge. Tell me, what is missing from the lions who guard the bridge of Lanchid?"

I knew the answer. I knew the tongues were what was missing, but I always let Papa tell me, and we would listen to his hearty laugh.

Soon we would reach the zoo. The balloon men and ice cream ladies lined the street in front of the entrance. "Hurry, hurry," one of them would shout. "It is feeding time for Hanna."

Hanna was a hippopotamus. Our city was famous for its hippos. They loved the warm springs that came naturally out of the ground, and they grew fat and healthy and had many babies that were sent to zoos all over the world.

230

Our city had built them a beautiful house in the zoo. It looked like a miniature palace, with copper domes and a large pool in front, and separate rooms with pools on the inside. Trees and flowers were planted around the hippo house, and the water was always kept clean.

Hanna was a special hippo. She liked being in the outside pool, close to the people. She often slept with one eye open, hoping that she would see the cart loaded with grass and hay creaking down the curved path. While the other hippos rested, she would get up just when the cart reached the giraffe house, next door. Hanna was the only hippo who was ready, mouth open, when the zookeeper had his first pitchfork full of hay poised in midair.

She would keep her mouth open until the keeper could get no more hay in, then, as fast as a hippo can, she would close her mouth. In a flash, it seemed, her mouth was open again, and all the hay was gone. The crowd would laugh, Papa loudest of all. That was one riddle even he could not figure out.

One winter, the river between the twin towns of
Buda and Pest froze. It was a big river, and the
winter had to be very cold for so much water to
freeze. But no one talked about it much, as
something much more important was happening to
us. There was a war going on, all over our part of
Europe, and beyond. There were now soldiers in
our town, on the banks of the river, and the soldiers
on either side were fighting each other.

The people would shake their heads, go to their
work, then come home and stay inside. Papa no
longer took us out on Sundays.

We sat by the hearth and studied our lessons and mended our worn clothing, and listened to the radio, hoping for better news. But the soldiers stayed, and the days grew colder. Our meat ran out, then our potatoes. Papa would come home with only a few onions and carrots from the market, and with these vegetables and sometimes with some thin chickens our neighbors gave us, Mama always managed to stretch our soup pot.

We were so busy thinking of our own hollow stomachs that Papa's news came as a surprise. "The animals in the zoo are hungry, too," he said. "I heard that because of the soldiers no food is coming into the town, and the animals need more food when winters are this cold." We thought of Hanna, and of her wide grin, and of how much hay her mouth could hold. We thought of her baby, born that summer, and of all of our famous hippos in the zoo. We went to bed that night feeling helpless and sad.

In the morning, Papa was in the kitchen, in his suit. His hands were in his pockets, and he had a big smile on his face. "We are going to the zoo," he said, "but not for fun. We are going to save the zoo today. If you children get dressed and come with me, I will show you how."

We scrambled to our rooms and in no time were back in the kitchen. Mama wrapped mufflers around our necks. The way she looked, we knew she and Papa had stayed up late thinking of a plan to save the hippos, and that it was a good one. On the way out of our house, Papa picked up our straw doormat and an old pair of straw slippers. Gabor, Eva, and I whispered together, but we knew Papa would share his secret only when he was ready.

On the way to the zoo, Papa told us what he and Mama had planned. "We are going to the zookeeper the first thing," he said. "And we will take him to the hippo house to show him the plan will work."

When we got to the hippo house, we could see a frozen pond and bare trees around it. The hippos were huddled inside for warmth and shelter from the wind. Hanna no longer looked our way, no longer slept with one eye open. We could hardly tell which hippo she was.

Papa walked up to the hunched animals and gently put the straw mat under the nose of one. The hippo moved but did not eat. So Papa got a pitchfork and broke the mat up and put the pieces of the old mat on the end of the fork. Then Papa offered our tattered mat to the hippo. The old hippo raised himself up and opened his mouth, and the mat was gone in a twinkling. "Well done," said the zookeeper. "Well done."

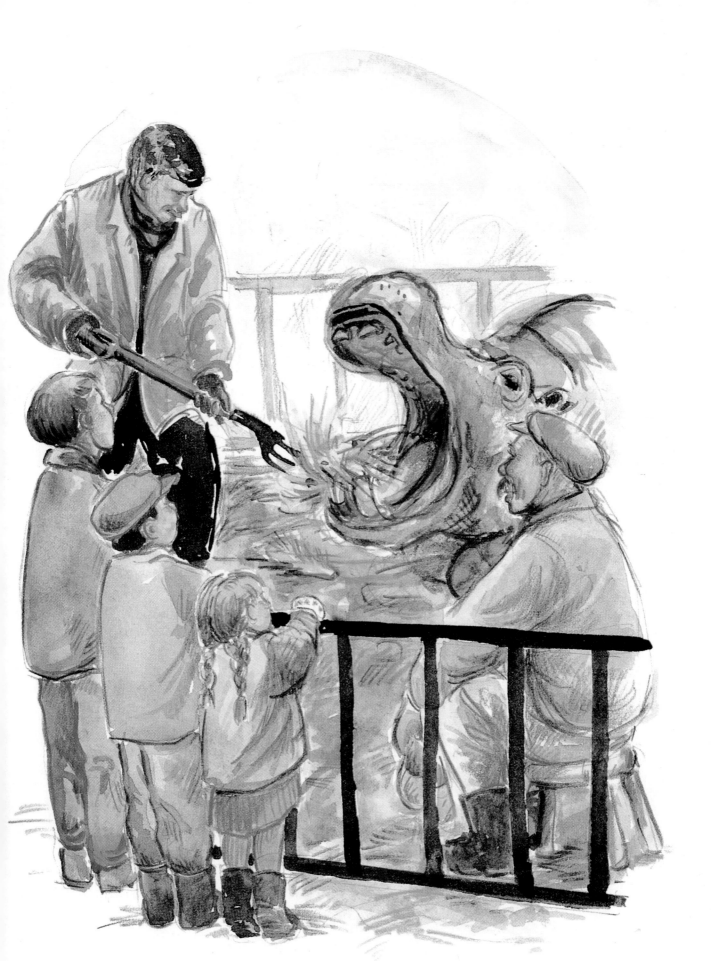

After that day, on cold nights and on gray mornings, in mist and in fog and in snow, an old cart pulled by an older horse traveled the streets of Buda and Pest. "Feed the hippos, straw for the hippos," the driver's voice echoed through the streets.

The people of my town ran out of their doors and piled their old straw mats and slippers and hats onto the cart. The cart was filled time and again, and the old horse faithfully pulled each load to Hanna and the other hippos at the zoo.

By the end of the winter, the people of Budapest had given nine thousand hats and mats and slippers to the hippos. The hippos did not grow fat, but the straw kept them alive through that cold and frightening winter.

The war in our town ended that spring. Now I am grown up, and the cold winter and the soldiers are only a memory. But the hippos in Budapest are still living in their palace and wallowing in the warm springs. I have traveled far since those days. Every time I see a hippo in a zoo someplace in the world, I think of Hanna, and of Papa and the brave people of my town, who saved their hippos during the war, with nine thousand straw slippers.

IN RESPONSE

Budapest Journal Write a journal entry as if you were Tibor, Gabor, or Eva. Talk about how the war makes life different. What is it like for you and your family? What is it like for the zoo animals?

Be a Tour Guide Draw and label a map of what you think the city of Budapest looks like. (Look back at the illustrations for ideas.) Then plan a Sunday outing for Tibor and his family.

Save the Hippos In a small group, discuss what else the people of Budapest might have done to save the hippos or other zoo animals. Share your ideas with the class.

If I were President

If I were President,

the tanks would be playhouses for the kids.

Boxes of candy would fall from the sky.

The mortars would fire balloons.

And the guns would blossom with flowers.

All the world's children

would sleep in a peace unbroken

by alerts or by shooting.

The refugees would return to their villages.

And we would start anew.

Poem by Roberto, 10,
from Pula, Croatia

Painting, *Poruke (Messages)*,
by Maja, 12,
from Požega, Croatia

Author and Illustrator at Work

Margaree King Mitchell was able to practice her writing and help her grandfather at the same time when she was young. In those days, very few people owned televisions. Most people listened to the radio to get the news. When her grandfather was too busy to listen to the news on the radio, she would listen and write down the news that she heard. Then, while her grandfather ate supper, Mitchell would read her news stories to him.

★ Award-winning Illustrator

When **James E. Ransome** illustrates a book, he tries to show that everyone has different, wonderful qualities that make them special. Like Uncle Jed in the story you are about to read, Ransome's father recently opened his own barbershop. He has worked as a barber for twenty-five years.

★ Award-winning Book

UNCLE JED'S BARBERSHOP

By Margaree King Mitchell • Illustrated by James Ransome

JEDEDIAH JOHNSON was my granddaddy's brother. Everybody has their favorite relative. Well, Uncle Jedediah was mine.

He used to come by our house every Wednesday night with his clippers. He was the only black barber in the county. Daddy said that before Uncle Jed started cutting hair, he and Granddaddy used to have to go thirty miles to get a haircut.

After Uncle Jed cut my daddy's hair, he lathered a short brush with soap and spread it over my daddy's face and shaved him. Then he started over on my granddaddy.

I always asked Uncle Jed to cut my hair, but Mama wouldn't let him. So he would run the clippers on the back of my neck and just pretend to cut my hair. He even spread lotion on my neck. I would smell wonderful all day.

When he was done, he would pick me up and sit me in his lap and tell me about the barbershop he was going to open one day and about all the fancy equipment that would be in it.

The sinks would be so shiny they sparkled, the floors so clean you could see yourself. He was going to have four barber chairs. And outside was going to be a big, tall, red-and-white barber pole. He told me he was saving up for it.

He had been saying the same thing for years. Nobody believed him. People didn't have dreams like that in those days.

We lived in the South. Most people were poor. My daddy owned a few acres of land and so did a few others. But most people were sharecroppers. That meant they lived in a shack and worked somebody else's land in exchange for a share of the crop.

When I was five years old, I got sick. This particular morning, I didn't come into the kitchen while Mama was fixing breakfast. Mama and Daddy couldn't wake me up. My nightgown and the bedclothes were all wet where I had sweated.

Mama wrapped me in a blanket while Daddy went outside and hitched the horse to the wagon. We had to travel about twenty miles into town to the hospital. It was midday when we got there. We had to go to the colored waiting room. In those days, they kept blacks and whites separate. There were separate public rest rooms, separate water fountains, separate schools. It was called segregation. So in the hospital, we had to go to the colored waiting room.

Even though I was unconscious, the doctors wouldn't look at me until they had finished with all the white patients. When the doctors did examine me, they told my daddy that I needed an operation and that it would cost three hundred dollars.

Three hundred dollars was a lot of money in those days. My daddy didn't have that kind of money. And the doctors wouldn't do the operation until they had the money.

My mama bundled me back up in the blanket and they took me home. Mama held me in her arms all night. She kept me alive until Daddy found Uncle Jed. He found him early the next morning in the next county on his way to cut somebody's hair. Daddy told him about me.

Uncle Jed leaned on his bent cane and stared straight ahead. He told Daddy that the money didn't matter. He couldn't let anything happen to his Sarah Jean.

Well, I had the operation. For a long time after that, Uncle Jed came by the house every day to see how I was doing. I know that three hundred dollars delayed him from opening the barbershop.

Uncle Jed came awfully close to opening his shop a few years after my operation. He had saved enough money to buy the land and build the building. But he still needed money for the equipment.

Anyway, Uncle Jed had come by the house. We had just finished supper when there was a knock on the door. It was Mr. Ernest Walters, a friend of Uncle Jed's. He had come by to tell Uncle Jed about the bank failing. That was where Mr. Walters and Uncle Jed had their money. Uncle Jed had over three thousand dollars in the bank, and it was gone.

Uncle Jed just stood there a long time before he said anything. Then he told Mr. Walters that even though he was disappointed, he would just have to start all over again.

Talk about some hard times. that was the beginning of the Great Depression. Nobody had much money.

But Uncle Jed kept going around to his customers cutting their hair, even though they couldn't pay him. His customer's gave him what they had—a hot meal, fresh eggs, vegetables from the garden. And when they were able to pay again, they did.

And Uncle Jed started saving all over again.

Ol' Uncle Jed finally got his barbershop. He opened it on his seventy-ninth birthday. It had everything, just like he said it would—big comfortable chairs, four cutting stations. You name it! The floors were so clean, they sparkled.

On opening day, people came from all over the county. They were Ol' Uncle Jed's customers. He had walked to see them for so many years. That day they all came to him.

I believe he cut hair all night and all the next day and the next night and the day after that! That man was so glad to have that shop, he didn't need any sleep.

Of course, I was there, too. I wouldn't have missed it for the world. When I sat in one of the big barber chairs, Uncle Jed patted the back of my neck with lotion like he always did. Then he twirled me round and round in the barber chair.

Uncle Jed died not long after that, and I think he died a happy man. You see, he made his dream come true even when nobody else believed in it.

He taught me to dream, too.

IN RESPONSE

The Perfect Barbershop Draw a picture of Uncle Jed's barbershop. Reread the descriptions in the story and illustrate the perfect barbershop for Uncle Jed. You might want to show the inside, the outside, or the street it's on.

Don't Give Up Imagine that you are Uncle Jed. Write a short speech telling people not to give up their dreams. Practice your speech a few times. Then say it for a small group of classmates.

Grand Opening Today With a partner or by yourself, plan the grand opening celebration for Uncle Jed's barbershop. Decide whom to invite and who will give speeches. What kind of decorations should there be? Don't forget that it's Uncle Jed's birthday!

HIGH HOPES

Lyric by Sammy Cahn
Music by James Van Heusen

Next time you're found
With your chin on the ground,
There's a lot to be learned,
So look around.

Just what makes that little ol' ant
Think he'll move that rubber tree plant;
Anyone knows an ant can't
   move a rubber tree plant.
But he's got HIGH HOPES,
He's got HIGH HOPES;
He's got high apple pie in the sky hopes.
So any time you're gettin' low,
'Stead of lettin' go,
Just remember that ant.
Oops! There goes another rubber tree plant.
Oops! There goes another rubber tree plant!
Oops! There goes another rubber tree plant!

Just what makes that lit-tle ol' ant___ Think he'll move that rub-ber tree plant; An-y-one knows an ant can't move a rub-ber tree plant. But he's got HIGH___ HOPES, He's got HIGH___ HOPES; He's got high ap-ple pie in the sky___ hopes. So an-y-time you're get-tin' low, 'Stead of let-in' go, Just re-mem-ber that ant. Oops! There goes an-oth-er rub-ber tree plant. *Oops! There goes an-oth-er rub-ber tree plant.* Oops! There goes an oth-er rub-ber tree plant!

Author and Illustrator at Work

★ Award-winning Author

 Beverly Cleary was a children's librarian for many years. The students who came to her library asked for funny books about children like themselves. Cleary was disappointed to find few books she could recommend to these students. That was when Cleary decided to write her own funny stories about "plain, ordinary boys and girls" like Ramona.

★ Award-winning Illustrator

 Gerry Gersten is well known for his caricatures. Caricatures are drawings of people that exaggerate the way a person looks to create humor. Gersten has always liked illustrated books best. In fourth grade, Gersten's teacher gave him a book to read. When he saw that the story had no pictures in it, he was so disappointed that he tried to give it back.

Ramona's Book Report

Written by
Beverly Cleary

Illustrated by
Gerry Gersten

Ramona's Book Report

from *Ramona Quimby, Age 8*

THE QUIMBY FAMILY WAS FULL OF WORRIES. The parents were worried about managing without a car while a new transmission was installed and even more worried about paying for it. Beezus was worried about a party she had been invited to, because boys had also been invited. She was afraid it would turn out to be a dancing party, and she felt silly trying to dance. Besides, eighth-grade boys acted like a bunch of little kids at parties. Ramona, still feeling weak, moped around the house for another day worrying about her book report. If she made it interesting, Mrs. Whaley would think she was showing off. If she did not make it interesting, her teacher would not like it.

On top of everything, Beezus happened to look at her father's head as he bent over his books at the dining-room table that evening. "Daddy, you're getting thin on top!" she cried out, shocked.

Ramona rushed to look. "Just a little thin," she said, because she did not want her father's feelings hurt. "You aren't bald yet."

Mrs. Quimby also examined the top of her husband's head. "It is a little thin," she agreed, and kissed the spot. "Never mind. I found a gray hair last week."

"What is this? A conference about my hair?" asked Mr. Quimby, and he grabbed his wife around the waist. "Don't worry," he told her. "I'll still love you when you're old and gray."

"Thanks a lot," said Mrs. Quimby, not wanting to think of herself as old and gray. They both laughed. Mr. Quimby released his wife and gave her a playful slap on the bottom, an act that amused and shocked his daughters.

Ramona had two feelings about this conversation. She did not want her father's hair to grow thin or her mother's hair to grow gray. She wanted her parents to stay exactly as they were for ever and ever. But oh, how good it was to see them be so affectionate with one another. She knew her mother and father loved one another, but sometimes, when they were tired and hurried, or when they had long, serious conversations after the girls had gone to bed, she wondered and worried, because she knew children whose parents had stopped loving one another. Now she knew everything was all right.

Suddenly Ramona felt so happy that a book report did not seem so difficult after all—if she could think of a way to make it interesting.

The book, *The Left-Behind Cat*, which Mrs. Whaley had sent home for Ramona to read for her report, was divided into chapters but used babyish words. The story was about a cat that was left behind when a family moved away and about its adventures with a dog, another cat, and some children before it finally found a home with a nice old couple who gave it a saucer of cream and named it Lefty because its left paw was white and because it had been left behind. Medium-boring, thought Ramona, good enough to pass the time on the bus, but not good enough to read during Sustained Silent Reading. Besides, cream cost too much to give to a cat. The most the old people would give a cat was half-and-half, she thought. Ramona required accuracy from books as well as from people.

"Daddy, how do you sell something?" Ramona interrupted her father, who was studying, even though she knew she should not. However, her need for an answer was urgent.

Mr. Quimby did not look up from his book. "You ought to know. You see enough commercials on television."

Ramona considered his answer. She had always looked upon commercials as entertainment, but now she thought about some of her favorites—the cats that danced back and forth, the dog that pushed away brand-X dog food with his paw, the man who ate a pizza, got indigestion, and groaned that he couldn't believe he ate the *whole* thing, the six horses that pulled the Wells Fargo bank's stagecoach across deserts and over mountains.

"Do you mean I should do a book report like a T.V. commercial?" Ramona asked.

"Why not?" Mr. Quimby answered in an absentminded way.

"I don't want my teacher to say I'm a nuisance," said Ramona, needing assurance from a grown-up.

This time Mr. Quimby lifted his eyes from his book. "Look," he said, "she told you to pretend you're selling the book, so sell it. What better way than a T.V. commercial? You aren't being a nuisance if you do what your teacher asks." He looked at Ramona a moment and said, "Why do you worry she'd think you're a nuisance?"

Ramona stared at the carpet, wiggled her toes inside her shoes, and finally said, "I squeaked my shoes the first day of school."

"That's not being much of a nuisance," said Mr. Quimby.

"And when I got egg in my hair, Mrs. Whaley said I was a nuisance," confessed Ramona, "and then I threw up in school."

"But you didn't do those things on purpose," her father pointed out. "Now run along. I have studying to do."

Ramona thought this answer over and decided that since her parents agreed, they must be right. Well, Mrs. Whaley could just go jump in a lake, even though her teacher had written, without wasting words, that she missed her. Ramona was going to give her book report any way she wanted. So there, Mrs. Whaley.

Ramona went to her room and looked at her table, which the family called "Ramona's studio," because it was a clutter of crayons, different kinds of paper, Scotch tape, bits of yarn, and odds and ends that Ramona used for amusing herself. Then Ramona thought a moment, and suddenly, filled with inspiration, she went to work. She knew exactly what she wanted to do and set about doing it. She worked with paper, crayons, Scotch tape, and rubber bands. She worked so hard and with such pleasure that her cheeks grew pink. Nothing in the whole world felt as good as being able to make something from a sudden idea.

Finally, with a big sigh of relief, Ramona leaned back in her chair to admire her work: three cat masks with holes for eyes and mouths, masks that could be worn by hooking rubber bands over ears. But Ramona did not stop there. With pencil and paper, she began to write out what she would say. She was so full of ideas that she printed rather than waste time in cursive writing. Next she phoned Sara and Janet, keeping her voice low and trying not to giggle so she wouldn't disturb her father any more than necessary, and explained her plan to them. Both her friends giggled and agreed to take part in the book report. Ramona spent the rest of the evening memorizing what she was going to say.

The next morning on the bus and at school, no one even mentioned Ramona's throwing up. She had braced herself for some remark from Yard Ape, but all he said was, "Hi, Superfoot." When school started, Ramona slipped cat masks to Susan and Janet, handed her written excuse for her absence to Mrs. Whaley, and waited, fanning away escaped fruit flies, for book reports to begin.

After arithmetic, Mrs. Whaley called on several people to come to the front of the room to pretend they were selling books to the class. Most of the reports began, "This is a book about . . ." and many, as Beezus had predicted, ended with ". . . if you want to find out what happens next, read the book."

Then Mrs. Whaley said, "We have time for one more report before lunch. Who wants to be next?"

Ramona waved her hand, and Mrs. Whaley nodded.

Ramona beckoned to Sara and Janet, who giggled in an embarrassed way but joined Ramona, standing behind her and off to one side. All three girls slipped on their cat masks and giggled again. Ramona took a deep breath as Sara and Janet began to chant, "*Meow*, meow, meow, meow. *Meow*, meow, meow, meow," and danced back and forth like the cats they had seen in the cat-food commercial on television.

"*Left-Behind Cat* gives kids something to smile about," said Ramona in a loud clear voice, while her chorus meowed softly behind her. She wasn't sure that what she said was exactly true, but neither were the commercials that showed cats eating dry cat food without making any noise. "Kids who have tried *Left-Behind Cat* are all smiles, smiles, smiles. *Left-Behind Cat* is the book kids ask for by name. Kids can read it every day and thrive on it. The happiest kids read *Left-Behind Cat: Left-Behind Cat* contains cats, dogs, people—" Here Ramona caught sight of Yard Ape leaning back in his seat, grinning in the way that always flustered her. She could not help interrupting herself with a giggle, and after suppressing it she tried not to look at Yard Ape and to take up where she had left off. ". . . cats, dogs, people—" The giggle came back, and Ramona was lost. She could not remember what came next. ". . . cats, dogs, people," she repeated, trying to start and failing.

Mrs. Whaley and the class waited. Yard Ape grinned. Ramona's loyal chorus meowed and danced. This performance could not go on all morning. Ramona had to say something, anything to end the waiting, the meowing, her book report.

She tried desperately to recall a cat-food commercial, any cat-food commercial, and could not. All she could remember was the man on television who ate the pizza, and so she blurted out the only sentence she could think of, "I can't believe I read the *whole* thing!"

Mrs. Whaley's laugh rang out above the laughter of the class. Ramona felt her face turn red behind her mask, and her ears, visible to the class, turned red as well.

"Thank you, Ramona," said Mrs. Whaley. "That was most entertaining. Class, you are excused for lunch."

Ramona felt brave behind her cat mask. "Mrs. Whaley," she said, as the class pushed back chairs and gathered up lunch boxes, "that wasn't the way my report was supposed to end."

"Did you like the book?" asked Mrs. Whaley.

"Not really," confessed Ramona.

"Then I think it was a good way to end your report," said the teacher. "Asking the class to sell books they really don't like isn't fair, now that I stop to think about it. I was only trying to make the book reports a little livelier."

Encouraged by this confession and still safe behind her mask, Ramona had the boldness to speak up. "Mrs. Whaley," she said with her heart pounding, "you told Mrs. Larson that I'm a nuisance, and I don't think I am."

Mrs. Whaley looked astonished. "When did I say that?"

"The day I got egg in my hair," said Ramona. "You called me a show-off and said I was a nuisance."

Mrs. Whaley frowned, thinking. "Why, Ramona, I can recall saying something about my little show-off, but I meant it affectionately, and I'm sure I never called you a nuisance."

"Yes, you did," insisted Ramona. "You said I was a show-off, and then you said, 'What a nuisance.'" Ramona could never forget those exact words.

Mrs. Whaley, who had looked worried, smiled in relief. "Oh, Ramona, you misunderstood," she said. "I meant that trying to wash egg out of your hair was a nuisance for Mrs. Larson. I didn't mean that you personally were a nuisance."

Ramona felt a little better, enough to come out from under her mask to say, "I wasn't showing off. I was just trying to crack an egg on my head like everyone else."

Mrs. Whaley's smile was mischievous. "Tell me, Ramona," she said, "don't you ever try to show off?"

Ramona was embarrassed. "Well . . . maybe . . . sometimes, a little," she admitted. Then she added positively, "But I wasn't showing off that day. How could I be showing off when I was doing what everyone else was doing?"

"You've convinced me," said Mrs. Whaley with a big smile. "Now run along and eat your lunch."

Ramona snatched up her lunch box and went jumping down the stairs to the cafeteria. She laughed to herself because she knew exactly what all the boys and girls from her class would say when they finished their lunches. She knew because she planned to say it herself. "I can't believe I ate the *whole* thing!"

In Response

Write Your Own Ad Think of a book you would like to recommend. Write a print advertisement for that book. Look at real ads to get ideas for using different-sized letters and words to show what's important. Then print your ad by hand or use a computer.

Draw Your Props Ramona made masks, to use as props for "selling" her book. Think of a book you would like to recommend. Draw some props, objects you could use in a performance, that would help you convince your classmates to read the book.

A Friend in Need The story does not tell us how Ramona convinced her friends to help her with her book report. What do you think she said to them? Role-play the phone conversations between Ramona and her friends Sarah and Grace. Think about what you would say if Ramona asked *you* to get up in front of the class.

An Artist's Challenge

Chuck Close paints pictures of people, such as *Kiki* and *Eric*. He paints his subjects by putting groups of little painted marks together. His challenge is made harder because he paints on a huge canvas. What do you see if you stand very close to the painting *Eric*? What happens when you look at *Eric* from a distance?

Kiki

Painting by Chuck Close (U.S.), 1993

Eric
Painting by
Chuck Close (U.S.),
1990

Chuck Close faces a tough challenge every
time he paints. He is quadriplegic, paralyzed
from the neck down. Here, he is working on
the painting *Eric*.

The Silver Bookcase

My Name is María Isabel

by Alma Flor Ada, illustrated by K. Dyble Thompson, translated from the Spanish by Ana M. Cerro, Atheneum, 1993

María Isabel doesn't like her new school. When her teacher insists on calling her Mary, she does not answer. María wonders if she will ever get her teacher to understand.

Lucky in Left Field

by Betsy Duffey, illustrated by Leslie Morrill, Simon & Schuster, 1992

George wants to win a baseball game, but he doesn't like some of the things the new coach does. In the end, George must decide whether winning is worth doing things he knows are wrong.

The Mapmaker's Daughter

by M. C. Helldorfer, illustrated by Jonathan Hunt, Bradbury Press, 1991

The mapmaker's daughter is eager for adventure. She goes on an exciting journey through an enchanted land to save the prince and the kingdom.

The All New Jonah Twist

by Natalie Honeycutt, Bradbury Press, 1986

Third-grader Jonah wants to be a star student like his older brother. But Jonah is a daydreamer and easily distracted. And the new "tough" boy in class isn't helping Jonah become an all new person.

Annie Pitts, Artichoke

by Diane deGroat, Simon & Schuster, 1992

Annie is looking forward to the lead role in the school play on nutrition. Instead, she is given the part of an artichoke. How much attention can an artichoke receive? If you're Annie—plenty!

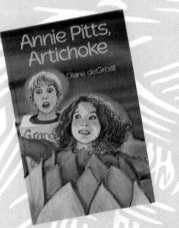

Glossary

Use this glossary to find the meanings and pronunciation of words in this book that may be new to you.

PRONUNCIATION KEY

Symbol	Key Words	Symbol	Key Words
a	cat	b	bed
ā	ape	d	dog
ä	cot, car	f	fall
e	ten	g	get
ē	me	h	help
i	fit	k	kiss, call
ī	ice	l	leg
ō	go	m	meat
ô	fall, paw	n	nose
oi	oil	p	put
oo	look, pull	r	red
o͞o	tool, rule	s	see
ou	out, crowd	t	top
u	up	w	wish
ʉ	fur, shirt	y	yard
ə	a *in* ago	z	zebra
	e *in* agent	ch	chin, arch
	i *in* pencil	ng	ring, drink
	o *in* atom	sh	she, push
	u *in* circus	th	thin, truth
		th	then, father
		zh	measure

A heavy stress mark ´ is placed after a syllable that gets a heavy, or primary, stress, as in **picture** (pik´ chər).

A light stress mark ´ is placed after a syllable that gets a weaker, or secondary, stress, as in **dictionary** (dik´ shə ner´ ē).

a·broad *adv.* ə brôd´ Outside a person's own country. I am traveling *abroad* this summer to visit my grandmother in France.

ac·cu·ra·cy *n.* ak´ yoor ə sē The fact of being accurate, or without mistakes. I checked my spelling words for *accuracy.*

af·ter·math *n.* af´ tər math The result of an event that causes harm. Those fallen trees are the *aftermath* of the tornado.

ag·i·tate *v.* aj´ ə tāt To stir or shake up; to disturb. A washing machine *agitates* the clothes.

anx·ious *adj.* angk´ shəs Having a strong desire; eager. She was *anxious* to get home.

ap·pe·tiz·er *n.* ap´ ə tī´ zər A small bit of a tasty food or drink served before a meal. Italian restaurants often serve garlic bread as an *appetizer.*

as·sur·ance *n.* ə shoor´ əns Something said or done to make a person more relaxed. I was glad to have the doctor's *assurance* that I would feel better soon.

as·ton·ish *v.* ə stän´ ish To surprise greatly or amaze. The children were *astonished* to see a giant fish driving the school bus.

bac·te·ri·a *n.* bak tir´ ē ə Living things that have one cell and can be seen only with a microscope. People have millions of *bacteria* in their bodies.

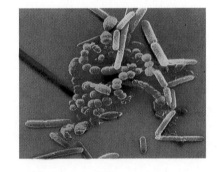

bald *adj.* bôld Having no hair on all or part of the head. If my father is *bald,* does that mean I will lose my hair when I get older?

boun·ty *n.* boun´ tē A reward; what you get from working hard. The farmer shared his *bounty* of corn with his friends.

appetizer

bald

bundle

clasp

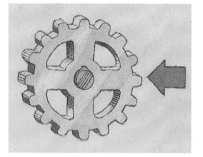

cog

bun·dle *v.* bun´ dəl To wrap or tie together. She *bundled* up her things and left.

chem·i·cal *n.* kem´ i kəl Something that is produced by or used in chemistry. Household cleaners are made of *chemicals.*

clasp *v.* klasp To hold tightly with the hand. Maria *clasped* the dog's collar so he wouldn't run out the door.

clut·ter *n.* klut´ ər A number of things scattered in a messy way. The *clutter* on the floor made it impossible to walk through the room.

cog *n.* käg A jagged part of a wheel in a machine that helps the machine move. The *cogs* on the wheels inside a clock make the hands turn.

coiled *adj.* koild Wound around and around in circles. The *coiled* hose looked like a sleeping snake.

com·fort·a·ble *adj.* kum´ fər ə bəl Cozy and relaxing. The sofa is so *comfortable* that anyone who sits on it soon falls asleep.

com·pas·sion *n.* kəm pash´ ə Feeling sorry for others and wanting to help them. The boy felt *compassion* for the hurt bir

con·fer·ence *n.* kän´ fər əns A meeting of people to discuss something. Mom went to the parent-teacher *conference* to fin out how I was doing in school.

a	cat	ō	go	u	fur, shirt
ā	ape	ô	fall, paw	ə	a *in* ago
ä	cot, car	oi	oil		e *in* agent
e	ten	oo	look, pull		i *in* pencil
ē	me	ōō	tool, rule		o *in* atom
i	fit	ou	out, crowd		u *in* circus
ī	ice	u	up		

core *n.* kôr The hard center of an apple, pear, and some other fruits. She ate all of the apple except the *core.*

crop *n.* kräp Food grown in the ground on a farm in large amounts. The farmer's most important *crop* is corn.

crude oil *n.* kro͞od oil Oil as it comes out of the ground. The tanker carried *crude oil* to the processing plant.

crush *v.* krush To press or squeeze with force. She *crushed* the gift box when she sat on it.

debris *n.* də brē′ What is left over after something has been broken, destroyed, or thrown away. The floor was covered with *debris* from the party.

del·i·cate *adj.* del′ i kət Easily hurt or broken; not strong. We washed the *delicate* dishes carefully.

de·spair *n.* də spār′ Loss of hope. We were filled with *despair* when our dog ran off and didn't come back.

dig·ni·ty *n.* dig′ ni tē Proud appearance or manner. Swans move with grace and *dignity.*

din *n.* din A loud, steady noise. The *din* of the crowd drowned out the president's speech.

di·ver·sion *n.* di vʉr′ zhən Something that draws your attention away from what you are doing. The two kittens playing were a *diversion* that kept me from my homework.

dome *n.* dōm A round roof that is shaped like half a globe. The Capitol in Washington, D.C., is a famous building with a *dome.*

drift *v.* drift To be carried along by the water or air. They watched the boat *drift* away from the dock and out to sea.

debris

dome

dusk

elder

flock

drought *n.* drout A long period of dry weather, with little or no rain. If the *drought* lasts any longer, all the crops will die.

dusk *n.* dusk The time of evening when it is beginning to get dark. The bats waited until *dusk* to leave their cave.

eld·er *n.* el´ dər An older person. We should all respect our *elders*.

en·core *n.* än´ kôr An extra performance given when an audience asks for more. The audience stood and clapped until the singer returned for an *encore*.

ex·pert *n.* eks´ pərt A person who knows a lot or has skill in a special area. My dad is a bird *expert*—he can name almost any bird that he sees in a picture.

a	cat	ō	go	ʉ	fur, shirt
ā	ape	ô	fall, paw	ə	a *in* ago
ä	cot, car	oi	oil		e *in* agent
e	ten	oo	look, pull		i *in* pencil
ē	me	ōō	tool, rule		o *in* atom
i	fit	ou	out, crowd		u *in* circus
ī	ice	u	up		

fad·ed *adj.* fād´ id Less brigh pale. The *faded* writing in the old book was difficult to read.

fan·cy *adj.* fan´ sē Not simple or plain; better than others; special. They lived in a *fancy* house with twenty-five rooms.

fen *n.* fen Low, flat, marshy land; swamp. They hunted for frogs in the *fen* behind the school.

flock *n.* fläk A group of animals that live, feed, and trav together. The shepherd guarded his *flock* of sheep.

flus·ter *v.* flus´ tər To make become excited or confused. Th winner was so *flustered* that he forgot his acceptance speech.

or·tune *n.* fôr´ chən A large
ım of money; wealth. He made
 fortune selling shovels the day
fter the blizzard.

oul *adj.* foul Having a bad
aste, smell, or appearance;
isgusting. We knew the milk
as bad because it had a *foul*
nell.

ra·grance *n.* frā´ grəns
 sweet or pleasant smell; odor.
he *fragrance* of the peeled
range filled the room.

rond *n.* fränd The leaf of a
rn or a palm tree. The ground
eneath the trees was covered
ith *fronds* after the storm.

ume *n.* fyōōm A gas or smoke
at is harmful or has a bad
nell. The paint *fumes* in the
ouse were so strong that we
ad to leave.

G

gap·ing *adj.* gāp´ ing Wide
open. The mouse chewed a
gaping hole in the wall.

gasp *v.* gasp To breathe in
suddenly in surprise, or to say
something while doing this. She
gasped when she saw the huge
birthday present.

gath·er *v.* gath´ ər To bring or
come together in one place or
group. He *gathered* all his toys
and put them away.

glo·ri·ous *adj.* glôr´ ē əs
Beautiful in a fantastic way;
wonderful. The rising sun was
a *glorious* sight.

grunt *v.* grunt To make a short,
deep sound. He *grunted* as he
lifted the heavy box.

H

har·vest *v.* här´ vəst To gather
a crop when it has finished
growing. She *harvested* the
tomatoes and got them ready to
go to market.

has·ten *v.* hās´ ən To go or act
quickly; to hurry. He *hastened*
home after school so he could
play soccer.

foul

gaping

harvest

hearth

hut

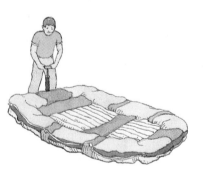

inflatable

haze *n.* hāz Mist, dust, or smoke in the air that makes it hard to see. The *haze* was so thick I couldn't see the end of the street.

hearth *n.* härth The stone or brick floor of a fireplace. She piled the logs on the *hearth* and started the fire.

hol·low *adj.* häl´ō Having an empty space on the inside; not solid. The statue is *hollow,* and it echoes inside if you knock on it.

a	cat	ō	go	ʉ	fur, shirt
ā	ape	ô	fall, paw	ə	a *in* ago
ä	cot, car	oi	oil		e *in* agent
e	ten	oo	look, pull		i *in* pencil
ē	me	ōō	tool, rule		o *in* atom
i	fit	ou	out, crowd		u *in* circus
ɪ	ice	u	up		

hut *n.* hut A little house. We built a *hut* out of cardboard to use as a clubhouse.

im·i·tate *v.* im´i tāt To copy the way someone looks, acts, or sounds. To get her dog's attention, she *imitates* a cat meowing.

im·pass·a·ble *adj.* im pas´ ə bəl Cannot be crossed or traveled over. An *impassable* wall protected the castle.

in·flat·a·ble *adj.* in flāt´ ə bə Gets bigger when filled with air or gas. The *inflatable* raft was big enough to carry four people

in·spi·ra·tion *n.* in´ spər ā´ shən Something or someone tha causes new feelings or thoughts. The *inspiration* for his story wa a joke his sister told him.

J

jeal·ous *adj.* jel´ əs Wanting what someone else has. I was *jealous* because she got a new bicycle and I didn't.

ket·tle *n.* ket´ l A metal pot for cooking. He boiled the water for tea in a copper *kettle.*

lum·ber *v.* lum´ bər To move slowly and clumsily because of great weight and size. The giant lumbered toward the village.

lus·cious *adj.* lush´ əs Having a wonderful taste or smell; full of flavor. The *luscious* oranges were a perfect dessert.

maze *n.* māz A pattern of paths, some of which lead nowhere, that is hard to follow. The mouse could not find its way through the *maze.*

mer·cy *n.* mur´ sē Great kindness to an enemy or a guilty person. The judge had *mercy* on the thief and did not send him to jail.

min·i·a·ture *adj.* min´ ē ə chər Very small in size or scale. My brother brought me a *miniature* Liberty Bell from Philadelphia.

mis·er·y *n.* miz´ ər ē Trouble; great sadness. Rain on our vacation caused us *misery.*

nim·ble *adj.* nim´ bəl Moving quickly and lightly. The *nimble* girl quickly climbed up the tree to rescue her cat.

nui·sance *n.* noo͞´ səns An act, thing, or person that causes trouble or bother. Our new puppy is a *nuisance* because he chews up everything in sight.

oc·cur *v.* ə kur´ To take place, happen. Did anything strange *occur* during your visit?

op·er·a·tion *n.* äp´ ər ā´shən An act done by surgeons in a hospital to make a person better or to save the person's life. My brother had an *operation* to have his tonsils removed.

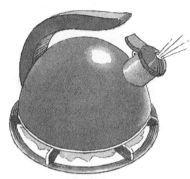

kettle

maze

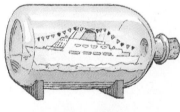

miniature

palace

pastry

polished

pal·ace *n.* pal´ əs The home of a king, queen, or other ruler, usually a large, grand building. He wished he were a king, living in a *palace.*

par·tic·i·pant *n.* pär tis´ ə pənt A person who takes part in something. "All *participants* in the race, come to the starting line!" called the announcer.

pas·try *n.* pās´ trē Pies, tarts, and other baked foods. She went to a *pastry* shop and bought an apple pie to bring to the picnic.

pe·cu·liar *adj.* pi kyo͞ol´ yər Odd or strange. That is a very *peculiar* dog—he never barks at all!

pee·vish·ly *adv.* pēv´ ish lē Done in a cross or cranky manner. Grumbling that it wasn't his turn, my brother *peevishly* took out the garbage.

pit·y *n.* pit´ ē A feeling of sadness for another's bad luck. She felt *pity* for the dog that someone left in the hot car.

a	cat	ō	go	u	fur, shirt
ā	ape	ô	fall, paw	ə	a *in* ago
ä	cot, car	oi	oil		e *in* agent
e	ten	oo	look, pull		i *in* pencil
ē	me	o͞o	tool, rule		o *in* atom
i	fit	ou	out, crowd		u *in* circus
ī	ice	u	up		

poise *v.* poiz To balance; to hang in midair. The owl *poised* itself on a tree branch, ready to swoop down on an unlucky mouse.

pol·ished *adj.* päl´ ishd Smooth and bright or shiny. Th freshly *polished* floor sparkled i the sunlight.

qual·i·ty *n.* kwôl´ i tē Havin great value or worth. The paint uses only paintbrushes of high *quality.*

rau·cous *adj.* rô´ kəs Sounding
loud or harsh. The crow's
raucous squawking woke me up
last night.

reed *n.* rēd A tall, slender
grass that grows along the edges
of lakes, streams, and marshes.
The ducklings followed their
mother through the *reeds* and
into the lake.

ref·uge *n.* ref´ yōoj A place
that protects from trouble or
danger. They found *refuge* from
the storm inside a cave.

re·lief *n.* rē lēf´ A good feeling
that replaces worry or fear. The
class sighed with *relief* when the
teacher decided not to give a
math test.

re·luc·tance *n.* rē luk´ təns
Not wanting to do something;
unwillingness. The move filled
her with *reluctance* because she
didn't want to leave her friends.

re·mark *n.* rē märk´ Something
that is said; a comment. I got in
trouble for making a rude
remark about his haircut.

re·spect *n.* rē spekt´ Polite
treatment; showing that someone
or something has value. If you
treat others with *respect,* they
will treat you the same way.

sad·dle *n.* sad´ əl A seat for a
rider on a horse or bicycle. He
almost fell off the horse, but he
managed to stay in the *saddle.*

sa·shay *v.* sa shā´ To walk or
move in a smooth and easy way.
The cat *sashayed* across the
room.

sau·cer *n.* sô´ sər A small dish,
especially one that is meant to
hold a cup. We gave the kitten a
saucer of milk.

scam·per *v.* skam´ pər To
move quickly or in a hurry. The
squirrels *scampered* up the tree.

scheme *v.* skēm To make
secret or dishonest plans; to plot.
He *schemed* to trick his brother
into washing the dishes.

scold *v.* skōld To speak angrily
at someone for something he or
she did. She *scolded* me for
being late.

se·rene·ly *adv.* sə rēn´ lē In a
calm or peaceful way. The fish
swam slowly and *serenely*
around the pond.

ser·pent *n.* sʉ´ pənt A large,
poisonous snake. The *serpent*
hissed as it crawled across the
sand.

reed

saddle

saucer

301

shingled

spring

steam

set·tle *v.* set´ l To get everyone to agree or decide. With my father's help, my mother and I *settled* our argument.

shel·ter *n.* shel´ tər Something that protects. We ran under the bus *shelter* to get out of the rain.

shin·gled *adj.* shing´ gəld Covered with thin, flat pieces of wood or other materials, usually on the roof or side of a house. We live in a gray *shingled* house with a red door.

shin·ny *v.* shin´ ē To climb by holding on with the hands and legs. She could *shinny* up the rope faster than anyone else in gym class.

a	cat	ō	go	ʉ	fur, shirt
ā	ape	ô	fall, paw	ə	a *in* ago
ä	cot, car	oi	oil		e *in* agent
e	ten	oo	look, pull		i *in* pencil
ē	me	o͞o	tool, rule		o *in* atom
i	fit	ou	out, crowd		u *in* circus
ī	ice	u	up		

shriek *n.* shrēk A loud cry; a screech; a scream. He let out a *shriek* of pain when he stepped on the tack.

spring *n.* spring A place whe water flows from the ground. They camped next to a *spring* they would have water to drink

steam *n.* stēm Water that ha been changed into a gas, usuall by being heated. *Steam* was rising from the kettle because t water inside was boiling.

stern *adj.* stʉrn Strict or hard not gentle or easygoing. The teacher was *stern* with the two children who were fighting.

stin·gy *adj.* stin´ jē Not willi to give or spend money; not kind. Don't ask her for money– she's *stingy*!

sud·den *adj.* sud´ n Happening or appearing withou warning; not expected. The *sudden* appearance of a rabbit surprised everyone but the magician.

sum·mit *n.* sum´ it The highest point; the top. It took them three days to reach the mountain's *summit.*

su·per·sti·tious *adj.* sōō´ pər ish´ əs Believing in things that are unreal or magical. *Superstitious* people believe that is bad luck for a black cat to cross your path.

sup·press *v.* sə pres´ To hold back. She *suppressed* a sneeze by holding her nose.

sus·tained *adj.* sə stānd´ Having gone on for a long time; continued. The *sustained* scream of the siren gave me a headache.

T

thrive *v.* thrīv To grow in a strong and healthy way. Cats *thrive* in loving homes.

tile *n.* tīl A thin piece of stone, baked clay, or plastic used to cover roofs, floors, or walls. The black and white *tiles* made the floor look like a checkerboard.

toil *v.* toil To work hard. The work crew *toiled* all night to finish the bridge on time.

U

un·con·scious *adj.* un kän´ shəs Not able to feel or think; not conscious. The *unconscious* man was rushed to the hospital.

ur·gent *adj.* ʉ´ jənt Needing quick action; important. No matter how small it is, a fire is always an *urgent* problem.

W

wallow *v.* wäl´ ō To roll about or lie in mud or dust the way some animals do. The pigs *wallowed* in the cool mud.

while *n.* hwīl A period of time. We sat in the waiting room for a short *while* before the doctor could see us.

Y

yelp *v.* yelp To give a short, sharp cry, like a dog in pain. She *yelped* as I pulled the splinter from her finger.

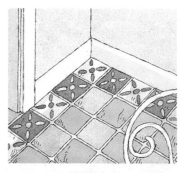
tile

wallow

ACKNOWLEDGMENTS

Grateful acknowledgment is made to the following publishers, authors, and agents for their permission to reprint copyrighted material. Every effort has been made to locate all copyright proprietors; any errors or omissions in copyright notice are inadvertent and will be corrected in future printings as they are discovered.

"Acorn" from **More Small Poems** by Valerie Worth. Copyright ©1976 by Valerie Worth. Reprinted by permission of Farrar, Straus & Giroux, Inc.

Anasi Finds a Fool by Verna Aardema. Copyright ©1992 by Verna Aardema. Used by permission of Curtis Brown Ltd. All rights reserved.

"And My Heart Soars" by Chief Dan George from **Voices on the Wind: Poems for All Seasons** selected by David Booth. Copyright ©1974 by Chief Dan George and Helmut Hirnschall. Reprinted by permission of Hancock House Publishing Ltd.

"The Ant and the Dove" from **Aesop's Fables** retold by Anne Gatti. Illustrated by Safaya Salter. Text copyright ©1992 by Pavilion Books, Ltd. Reprinted by permission of Harcourt Brace & Company.

Dear World by Lannis Temple. Copyright ©1992 by Lannis Temple. Used by permission of the American publisher, Random House, Inc., and the British publisher, Random Century Australia Pty. Ltd.

Hanna's Cold Winter by Trish Marx. Illustrated by Barbara Knutson. Text copyright 1993 by Trish Marx. Illustrations copyright 1993 by Carolrhoda Books, Inc. Used by permission of the publisher. All rights reserved.

"High Hopes" words by Sammy Cahn, music by James Van Heusen. Copyright ©1959 Sincap Productions, Inc. Copyright ©1959 (Renewed) Maraville Music Corp. All rights reserved. Made in USA. Used by permission of Warner Bros. Publications Inc., Miami, FL 33014.

"I May, I Might, I Must" from **The Complete Poems of Marianne Moore** by Marianne Moore. Copyright ©1959 by Marianne Moore, copyright renewed 1987 by Lawrence E. Brinn and Louise Crane, Executors of the Estate of Marianne Moore. Used by permission of Viking Penguin, a division of Penguin Books USA Inc.

"If I Were President" and "Poruke" by Roberto from **I Dream of Peace: Images of War by Children of Former Yugoslavia** by Maja and preface by Maurice Sendak. Copyright ©1994 UNICEF. Reprinted by permission of HarperCollins Publishers, Inc.

Just a Dream by Chris Van Allsburg. Copyright ©1990 by Chris Van Allsburg. Reprinted by permission of Houghton Mifflin Co. All rights reserved.

The Magical Starfruit Tree by Rosalind C. Wang. Paintings by Shao Wei Liu. Text copyright ©1993 by Rosalind C. Wang. Illustrations copyright ©1993 by Shao Wei Liu. Used by permission of the publisher, Beyond Words Publishing, Inc.

Ma'ii and Cousin Horned Toad: A Traditional Navajo Story by Shonto Begay. Copyright ©1992 by Shonto Begay. Reprinted by permission of Scholastic Inc.

Oil Spill! by Melvin Berger. Text copyright ©1994 by Melvin Berger. Illustrations copyright ©1994 by Paul Mirocha. Reprinted by permission of HarperCollins Publishers.

"The Other Frog Prince" from **The Stinky Cheese Man and Other Fairly Stupid Tales** by Jon Scieszka, illustrated by Lane Smith. Copyright ©1992 by Jon Scieszka, text, and copyright ©1992 by Lane Smith, illustrations. Used by permission of Viking Penguin, a division of Penguin Books USA Inc.

"Ramona's Book Report" from **Ramona Quimby, Age 8** by Beverly Cleary. Copyright ©1981 by Beverly Cleary. By permission of the American publisher, Morrow Junior Books, a division of William Morrow & Company, Inc. and of the British publisher, Hamish Hamilton Ltd.

The Singing Snake by Stefan Czernecki and Timothy Rhodes, illustrated by Stefan Czernecki. Text copyright ©1993 by Stefan Czernecki and Timothy Rhodes. Illustrations copyright ©1993 by Stefan Czernecki. Reprinted by permission of Hyperion Books for Children. All rights reserved.

There's so much that we share,... from "It's a Small World" words and music by Richard M. Sherman and Robert M. Sherman. ©1963 Walt Disney Music Company. Copyright renewed. All rights reserved.

Uncle Jed's Barbershop by Margaree King Mitchell. Illustrated by James Ransome. Text copyright ©1993 by Margaree King Mitchell. Illustrations copyright ©1993 by James Ransome. Reprinted with permission of Simon & Schuster Books for Young Readers, Simon & Schuster Children's Publishing Division.

The Woman Who Outshone the Sun by Rosalma Zubizarreta, based on a poem by Alejandro Cruz Martinez. Illustrations by Fernando Olivera. Story copyright ©1991 by Children's Book Press and Rosalma Zubizarreta. Pictures copyright ©1991 by Fernando Olivera. Used by permission of the publisher, Children's Book Press. All rights reserved.

COVER: Cover Design, Art Direction and Production, Design Five; Photography, Jade Albert Studio; Illustration, Kevin Hawkes.

ILLUSTRATION: 4, Alan Brunettin (t.l.); James Grashow (b.); 4–5, Amy Zerner (top bar); 6–7, Robert Giusti (top bar); 7, Amy Cordova (b.r.); 8–9 (top bar) Stephen Johnson; 9, Gerry Gersten (t.r.); 10–13, Amy Zerner; 14–15, 3-D illustration by Alan Brunettin; 38, 3-D illustration by Alan Brunettin (b.); 39, Bill Mayer (b.); 40–63, (all) James Grashow; 64–65, Viv Eisner-Hess; 92–93 (all) Mercedes McDonald; 119, Ligature (t.); 122–123, Background illustration by Cristine Mortenson; (border) Amy Zerner; 124–127, Robert Giusti; 154–155, Jerzy Kolacz; 186–187, Tracy Rea; 210–211, Amy Cordova; 212–213, Background illustration by Cristine Mortenson; (border) Robert Giusti; 214–217, Stephen Johnson; 268–269, 3-D illustration by Mark Steele; 271, (Ramona's face and book cover) Gerry Gersten; 272–286, (all) Gerry Gersten; 290–291, Background illustration by Cristine Mortenson; (border) Stephen Johnson; 293–303, (all) David Maloney

PHOTOGRAPHY: Unless otherwise indicated, photographs of book covers were provided by Ulsaker Studio, Inc. The abbreviation SBG stands for Silver Burdett Ginn. Photo styling for selection openers provided by Anne Bugatch and Lance Salemo. Unless otherwise indicated, Fine Art Portfolio frames © SBG, photo by Allan Penn. 4, © SBG, photo of illustration by Dave Bradley (t.l.); 6–7, (leaf) © SBG, photo by Allan Penn; 9, © Bill Jacobson/Photograph courtesy of The Pace Gallery, NY (b.r.); 14, Courtesy of Tim Rhodes (b.l.); Photo by P. Strakowski, Courtesy of Stefan Czernecki (t.l.); 14–15, photo of 3-D illustration by Dave Bradley; 38, © SBG, photo of 3-D illustration by Dave Bradley (b.); 40, Courtesy of Verna Aardema (t.l.); Photo by Linda Post, Courtesy of James Grashow (b.l.); 40–41, © SBG, photo by Allan Penn; 66, Courtesy of Scholastic Inc. (t.l.); 66–67, © SBG, photo by Allan Penn; 94, Courtesy of Rosalind Wang (t.l.); Courtesy of Shao Wei Lui (b.l.); 94–95, (all starfruit) © SBG, photo by Allan Penn; 119, (all starfruit) © SBG, photo by Allan Penn; 128, Courtesy of Clarion Books (t.l.); 128–129, © SBG, photo by Allan Penn; 153, © SBG, photo by Allan Penn (t.r.); 156, Courtesy of Melvin Berger (t.l.); Courtesy of Paul Mirocha (b.l.); 156–157, © SBG, photo by Allan Penn; 181, © SBG, photo by Doug Mindell; 184, National Museum of American Art, Washington DC/Art Resource, NY (l.); 186, Children's Book Press (l.); 186–187, © SBG, photo by Allan Penn; 218, Courtesy of Carolrhoda Books (t.l.,b.l.); 218–219, © SBG, photo by Allan Penn; 241, © SBG, photo by Allan Penn (b.); 244, Courtesy of Margeree King Mitchell (t.l.); Courtesy of Simon & Schuster (b.l.); 244–245, © SBG, photo by Allan Penn; 267, (background leaf) © SBG, photo by Allan Penn; 268–269, © SBG, photo of 3-D illustration by Allan Penn; 270, Margaret Miller, Courtesy of William Morrow and Company (t.l.); Courtesy of Gerry Gersten (b.l.); 270–271, © SBG, photo by Allan Penn; 287, © SBG, photo by Allan Penn; 288, Photo by Ellen Page Wilson/Pace Wildenstein collection Walker Art Center, Minneapolis gift of Judy and Kenneth Dayton,1994; 289, (all) © Photograph by Bill Jacobson, courtesy of The Pace Gallery, NY; 293, © David M. Phillips/Photo Researchers (c.l.); 296, © Kenneth Murray/Photo Researchers (t.l.); © Peter Pearson/Tony Stone Images (c.r.); 297, © Charles Krebs/Tony Stone Images (b.l.); 298, © Grandadam/Tony Stone Images (r.); 300, © Erik Svenson/Tony Stone Images (b.l.); 302, © Robert J. Ashworth/Photo Researchers (c.l.); © Michael Newman/Photo Edit (b.r.); 303, © George Mars Cassidy/Tony Stone Images (b.)